INTRODUCTION TO
Computational
Metagenomics

INTRODUCTION TO
Computational
Metagenomics

Zhong Wang

DOE Joint Genome Institute, USA &
Lawrence Berkeley National Lab, USA

 **World Scientific**

NEW JERSEY · LONDON · SINGAPORE · BEIJING · SHANGHAI · HONG KONG · TAIPEI · CHENNAI · TOKYO

Published by

World Scientific Publishing Co. Pte. Ltd.
5 Toh Tuck Link, Singapore 596224
USA office: 27 Warren Street, Suite 401-402, Hackensack, NJ 07601
UK office: 57 Shelton Street, Covent Garden, London WC2H 9HE

Library of Congress Cataloging-in-Publication Data
Names: Wang, Zhong (Computational biologist), author.
Title: Introduction to computational metagenomics / Zhong Wang.
Description: Hackensack, NJ : World Scientific Publishing, [2022] |
    Includes bibliographical references and index.
Identifiers: LCCN 2022000612 | ISBN 9789811242465 (hardcover) |
    ISBN 9789811242472 (ebook for individuals) | ISBN 9789811242489 (ebook for institutions)
Subjects: MESH: Metagenomics--methods | Computational Biology--methods
Classification: LCC QH447 | NLM QU 26.5 | DDC 572.8/629--dc23/eng/20220131
LC record available at https://lccn.loc.gov/2022000612

British Library Cataloguing-in-Publication Data
A catalogue record for this book is available from the British Library.

For any available supplementary material, please visit
https://www.worldscientific.com/worldscibooks/10.1142/12425#t=suppl

Typeset by Stallion Press
Email: enquiries@stallionpress.com

Preface

I heard the name "metagenomics" for the first time in my life when I
joined the Department of Energy's Joint Genome Institute (JGI) in 2009.
I was no stranger to microbiology or genomics, as I majored in microbiology in college and spent a significant portion of my graduate studies
in genomics and bioinformatics. It is just a scaled-up version of microbiology using genomics tools, I thought naively at that time. I could
never imagine the scale of the challenges and the impact it brings at
such a rapid pace. Just a few years later, metagenomics had already
taken a center stage — Science magazine named it as one of the breakthroughs of the year in both 2011 and 2013. Neither could I imagine
the amount of fun and learning experience I had since then.

As Harvard entomologist, Edward O. Wilson stated in his book *Consilience: The Unity of Knowledge* that modern science is increasingly
seeing the convergence of knowledge across separated disciplines, this
consilience process is also happening between metagenomics and data
science. The rapid development of metagenomics was propelled by a
tsunami of next-generation sequencing data, which offers an unprecedented opportunity for scientists to get a holistic view of a microbial
community and its intricate inner workings. This group of scientists,
mostly microbiologists, were also overwhelmed by the scale of the
metagenomics datasets and intimidated by the complexity to navigate
the richness of these data. They desperately needed help to understand
the data they generated. Fortunately, a new breed of data scientists,
while sailing in the ocean of big data, also discovered that their knowledge and experience could be well applied to the metagenomics data

problem. When the two camps joined forces, the field of computational metagenomics was born.

The three pillars of computational metagenomics

After these two camps of pioneers, both experts in their fields but speaking two different languages finally figured out a way to communicate with each other, they found that most of the computational metagenomics problems are more complex than each camp had individually envisioned. Solving a typical computational metagenomics problem, as it turns out, is analogous to planning a trip to a new destination. They need to know the terrain, but their map does not have sufficient information. Many roads are not labeled, some even contain errors. They need vehicles, but existing vehicles have various mechanical problems, and some even need to be broken apart and redesigned from scratch. They also need creative routes to overcome the uncertain map and unreliable vehicles to make sure they may eventually reach their destinations, or just get close enough. Here, the terrain refers to metagenomics, the study of microbial communities with many species, the majority of which could be unknown ones. Operating vehicle refers to data engineering, or dealing with scalable data collection, transformation, and analysis. Finally, routes refer to computer algorithms that correctly and efficiently solve problems. Thanks to the audacious efforts of these pioneers, advances in these three aspects now form the three pillars of computational metagenomics (Figure 1). Almost all computational metagenomics projects are built upon three pillars across different stages from planning to execution.

Although many computational metagenomics projects begin with some data already acquired, it is crucial to understand the scientific metagenomics questions and the experimental genome technologies that produce the data. This is a perquisite for every successful computational metagenomics project. For a given microbial community, do we want to know what organisms are present in the community? Or do we want to fish out interesting gene clusters for our engineering starting points? These scientific questions determine the genome technology to be used, the type of data to be generated, and the amount of data is needed. Each technology inevitably brings unique biases and noises,

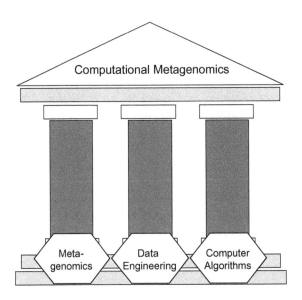

Fig. 1 The three pillars for computational metagenomics.

understanding them will guide us to design appropriate algorithms and statistics for robust data analysis.

Most research teams do not have a data architect to help us design a comprehensive strategy for data management and analytic, but this does not necessarily mean that we should ignore the data engineering aspect. Do we want to store the data on the cloud or locally? Do we need a workstation with more CPU cores or more memory? Do we need GPUs or a high-performance computing cluster to accelerate our software pipeline? A careful data plan can greatly shorten the time between data and scientific insights. Choice of different engineer solutions will bring different cost models in both computational and time. Many projects headed by biologists traditionally only include experimental costs but not computational costs, a hindsight often causes poor data management problems.

Having a fast computer loaded with CPUs and RAM does not guarantee a fast solution to our computational metagenomics problem, neither does it guarantee a correct one. This is where the computer algorithms come into play. Many problems, such as metagenome assembly, are so complex that it not only requires many computing nodes but also a special data structure to reach an approximate solution efficiently.

The main goal of this book is to introduce you to the three pillars of computational metagenomics. As a future leader in the field of computational metagenomics, you need to be a "jack-of-all-trades" when the time comes to collaborate with a team of microbiologist, hardware architects, software engineers, and data scientists.

Targeted audience

The book is written with the mind of targeting college seniors or first-year graduate students. It should serve some data engineering principles and a basic understanding of the underlying computational algorithms if you come from microbial genomics fields. If your background is in computation instead, I hope this book may help you get familiar with genome technologies so that you may apply your skills to solve some of the challenging metagenomics problems.

What will not be covered in this book

Although computational metagenomics relies heavily on various databases and software pipelines, in this book I will purposefully avoid the vast majority of them. The reason is two folds. Firstly, new databases and pipelines emerge rapidly as the field of metagenomics research proliferates, it is simply impossible to even briefly describe all of them. Even if I were able to do that, it would make the book hard to read. Secondly, most of the tools will become obsolete in a few years, even though the principles they build upon stay. Thus, I will focus on explaining the basic concepts behind these tools, and occasionally using a few representative tools as examples. With these knowledge, readers should get comfortable to read review papers about these databases and methods, as every year we see many such papers. The same idea applies to the research literature, as this book is never intended to provide a comprehensive review of any subfield in metagenomics. A Google Scholar search for papers with the keyword "metagenomics" returns 21,500 hits between 2007–2020. As a Chinese proverb says, "Give a man a fish and you feed him for a day. Teach a man to fish and you feed him for a lifetime". I will try my best to teach you fishing rather than giving you fish in this book.

To make the book more readable to a more general audience, I will also purposely omit many technical jargons, as many of them only appease experts in specific fields. Whenever I have to use one, I will try to explain it in the same context.

Structure of the book

Chapters 1–3 introduce the basic concepts in computational metagenomics from a metagenomics, data, and algorithm perspective, respectively. Because many computational metagenomics problems are big data problems, Chapter 4 is devoted to topics related to hardware and software platforms for scalable data analysis. These four chapters lay the ground for computational metagenomics and are an essential reading for beginners.

Chapter 5 provides an in-depth overview of data quality improvement, which is a common topic of almost all computational metagenomics projects. Chapters 6–10 each focus on a special topic: Chapter 6 on taxonomic diversity, Chapter 7 on functional diversity, Chapter 8 on metagenome assembly, Chapter 9 on single-cell metagenomics, and Chapter 10 on interactions between microbes and their environment. Each of these chapters itself is a mini-review of a single topic that can be read independently of each other. The content inside a chapter does not follow a strict structure, but it is loosely organized in four sections: background information, challenges, solutions, and future perspectives. These chapters are designed for more advanced readers, but it can also help beginners who want to cover more depth.

Given the broad applications of metagenomics, these topics are by no means definitive or comprehensive but serve as a starting point. It serves as an introduction to aspects of computational metagenomics and an invitation to a deep understanding of the biological algorithms that govern microbial life and their interactions.

Zhong Wang

Acknowledgments

Thanks to Qian and to Roger, for your patience on my long days and evenings at the keyboard. Your support gives me courage to be able to concentrate on writing amid an unsettling pandemic. Special thanks to Chris Davis, my fabulous acquisitions editor, who met me a couple of times spanning three years, and whose persistence nudged me to start this book project. Numerous thanks to my passionate production editor Ling Xiao, for her numerous and tireless edits.

Several graduate students have suffered crude early drafts of the book, and their constructive suggestions made it more bearable. These include Harrison Ho, Lucia-Bazan Williamson from the University of California at Merced, Chen Zhang and Xiao Liu from the Shanghai University in China.

I would like to thank my JGI colleagues for their generous help and their contributions to this book. Specifically, Dr. Simon Roux for sharing unpublished manuscripts and reference papers on phage-host identification for me to quickly become familiar with this topic; Dr. Robert Riley for contributing a poem about the future of metagenome assembly.

Special thanks to Prof. Yuzhen Ye at Indiana University, whose critical feedback provided me a chance to review some important literature, especially in the area of pathway analysis. This fills a big gap in the coverage of the book.

Contents

Chapter 1

Computational Metagenomics: A Metagenomics Perspective

Most of microorganisms are *small*, invisible to human eyes, and some even invisible to optical microscopes. Yet microbes are everywhere: they present in the air we breathe in, in the water we drink, and in the food we eat. They flourish on the surface of our skin and colonize in our gut. They outnumber our own cells: an average person has about 30 trillion human cells accompanied with 38 trillions bacteria, according to a recent estimation (Sender *et al.*, 2016). It is not possible to separate them from us, as they are a part of us. We exchange these microorganisms with other people and our environment all time. It is hard to imagine the extent of such exchanges, but a 10-second intimate kiss with a partner would mean 80 million bacteria are exchanged!

What are these microorganisms living within and around us? What do they do? How do they interact with us and among themselves? These are central questions in *metagenomics*, a rapidly evolving scientific discipline started only a couple of decades ago. In this chapter, I will introduce the concept of metagenomics, followed by the sequencing technologies currently employed to interrogate metagenomics. Getting to know these technologies is important to understand the metagenomics pillar of computational metagenomics.

1.1 Metagenome and Metagenomics

Just like us, microbial organisms also form social communities. A microbial community refers to all microbial organisms, including archaea, bacteria, fungi, protozoa, and viruses that live in a given habitat. These communities adapt to their environment together, some are associated with animals or plants, some freely live in water, air, or land. Their complexity at the taxonomic level, or the number of different species they contain, can vary greatly. A simple community such as an acid mine drainage biofilm contains only five species, while complex communities such as those from forest soils can contain tens of thousands of species (Tyson *et al.*, 2004).

A genome refers to the entire set of genetic information of a single organism, be it a bacterium or a human individual. A metagenome refers to the collective genetic information of a microbial community of a particular habitat. The collective microbial species in a community is also called microbiota or microbiome. A metagenome is not to be confused with a pangenome. A metagenome is the union of all genomes of all members of a microbial community, and the members may or may not be related. For example, the metagenome of the above-mentioned acid mine drainage community includes a few bacterial and archaeal species that cooperate to tolerate extreme environmental stress. Some of them are related but some are not. Metagenome is often studied in the context of microbial ecology. A pangenome, in contrast, only exists as a concept. It is the union of all genomes of a particular taxonomic group. For example, the pangenome of *E. coli* is defined by all genomes from all *E. coli* strains. A pangenome is often studied in the context of understanding genome evolution and diversification.

A closely related but slightly different concept is the microbiome. As a biome is a community of plants and animals that live in a habitat, a microbiome is its microbial counterpart. Therefore, the metagenome is the genome of a microbiome. Some people also use "microbiome" where "metagenome" should be used, ignoring the distinction that "metagenome" refers to genetic information, but the microbiome refers to biological materials. It is also worth noting that clinical researchers often "hijacked" the microbiome concept to narrowly refer it to the microbiome that lives on and inside the human body.

Metagenomics is the study of metagenomes. Many readers are already familiar with microbiology, in which microbiologists isolate and grow one or a few microbial organisms in the lab and study them. Modern microbiology has shifted from studying morphology features, growth, and metabolism to molecular characterization of its genomics information. For example, phylogenomic analysis precisely places a species on the tree of life, while homology-based gene discovery can quickly predict new members of protein families. Is metagenomics modern microbiology in parallel mode? The answer is both yes and no. Yes, in metagenomics we can ask almost the same set of questions regarding to many microbes simultaneously. Metagenomics questions can be much harder than a simple multiplication of a single-genome question, as you will see later chapters in this book, because physically or informatically separating the community members faces great technical challenges. In addition, as you will see below, metagenomics brings new dimensions that traditional microbiology fails to reach.

1.2 Metagenomics: Key Scientific Questions

In metagenomics, we ask scientific questions like the following (Boon *et al.*, 2014): What species are present in the microbial community of interest? What are their functions in the community? How does their abundance change in response to environmental changes? How are the species interacting with each other? I will use a few examples to show key questions asked in metagenomics in this section. The list of scientific questions in metagenomics one can ask does not stop here, though. Curious readers can read articles such as "Fifty important research questions in microbial ecology" (Antwis *et al.*, 2017) to explore the broad scope of metagenomics. Below I will list a few key questions in metagenomics, and for each question I will find a couple of inspiring science stories.

1.2.1 *Who is out there?*

Just like Charles Darwin's journey in the nineteenth century to discover new species, Craig Venter and a group of researchers in 2004 set out to the Sargasso Sea in the middle of the Atlantic Ocean near Bermuda. Venter knew that microorganisms in the world's oceans, like those in many other territories, are largely unexplored. In this first ever large-scale metagenomics study, his team produced a total of 1.045 gigabases of sequence derived from at least 1,800 different species from seawater samples they collected while circling the globe in Venter's luxury yacht the *Sorcerer II*. Among them, 148 had never been seen before (Venter *et al.*, 2004). Encouraged by the success of this pilot, Venter and his colleagues continued their Sorcerer II Global Ocean Sampling (GOS) Expedition for more than two years, visiting 23 different countries and island groups on four continents. These efforts led to the discovery of millions of new genes and nearly 1,000 genomes for uncultivated lineages of microbes, greatly expanded our knowledge of microbial diversity in the ocean (https://www.jcvi.org/research/gos).

Venter's epic GOS study broke the dawn of a new metagenomics era. Previously, more than 88% of all microbial species discovered via cultivation belong to only four bacterial phyla (Proteobacteria, Firmicutes, Actinobacteria, and Bacteroidetes), while half of the 60 major branches of the tree of life lack any isolated representatives. In another historical landmark study, a research team led by the US Department of Energy (DOE) Joint Genome Institute (JGI)'s Tanja Woyke systematically sequenced more than 200 uncultivated archaeal and bacterial cells from a variety of habitats. The approach they took is called single-cell metagenomics, which we will review in Chapter 9. In this single study, they discovered new species from more than 20 major branches of the tree of life. These new species likely represent only the tip of the iceberg of undiscovered microbial diversity, or the so-called "microbial dark matter" (Rinke *et al.*, 2013).

1.2.2 *What are they doing?*

Craig Venter's expedition was funded by a $9 million grant award from DOE to the Institute for Biological Energy Alternatives (IBEA), which Venter heads. Besides "may lead to the development of new methods for carbon sequestration or alternative energy production", DOE also hoped that this study may uncover new microbial genes that support the energy needs of their hosts to efficiently turn sunlight into energy. These mechanisms could also be harnessed to pave the way to better biofuels.

With metagenomics, the bioprospecting process, or exploring natural sources for commercially valuable product candidates, can be greatly accelerated. In 2011, a team lead by JGI's Eddy Rubin sequenced and analyzed 268 gigabases of metagenomic DNA from microbes in cow rumen, and they identified 27,755 candidate enzymes that could be exploited further for their ability for converting biomass to energy (Hess *et al.*, 2011).

The action of these microbes is not limited to impact carbon cycling and energy conversion in our environment, and recent studies started to reveal the role of our "second genome" (the microbiome) that lives within us. The human gut microbiome not only impacts our nutrition, but also affects the efficacy and toxicity of the medicine we take. Some produce compounds that can lead to new therapeutics, qualifying them as "the microbial pharmacists within" (Spanogiannopoulos *et al.*, 2016).

1.2.3 *How do they interact?*

Besides directly impacting health and disease treatment, species among the microbiome are also interacting with each other and form intricate networks that indirectly impact their host's health (Gould *et al.*, 2018). An imbalance of microbes in our gut has long believed to lead to immune related health problems (Kho and Lal, 2018). A recent study found that imbalance in the gut microbiome contributes to the severity of COVID-19 (Yeoh *et al.*, 2021). The list of cases implicating microbiome in health is growing rapidly.

1.3 Metagenome Sequencing: Strategies

To answer the above scientific questions, today's microbial ecologists seldom rely on traditional methods of identification and isolation to study microbial communities. Just like we sequence the human genome to understand our own species, *Homo sapiens*, we use DNA sequencing to understand the members of a microbial community. Sequencing not only provides more insights than microscopy in understanding microbial diversity but also has the potential to shed light on their metabolic capacity by constructing genome-scale metabolic models (GEMs, a topic we will visit in Chapter 10). In contrast to individual microbial genome sequencing that we sequence cultured single isolates, in metagenome sequencing, we sequence a microbial community directly isolated from the environment without cultivation. This is particularly important given the fact that it is estimated that only

1% of the microbial population is amenable to be cultivated in the lab environment (Staley and Konopka, 1985), due to either unknown culture conditions or their dependencies on other species. The application of high-throughput sequencing directly to environmental samples has enabled analyses at unprecedented scale and speed, bringing a generic method to study almost any microbial community in any habitat, even in the International Space Station (Nicholas *et al.*, 2017). Designing these high-throughput metagenomics experiments to be statistically robust and reproducible, however, is no trivial task. We will not cover the art of experimental design here in this book, as it depends heavily on specific scientific problems and available resources. We will only discuss briefly the technologies underlying computational metagenomics. Readers are encouraged to read a comprehensive review article by Knight *et al.* to gain in-depth knowledge about metagenomics experimental design (Knight *et al.*, 2012).

Numerous sequencing strategies and techniques have been developed in the past 15 years. I will attempt to briefly summarize these exciting developments below. Depending on the scientific question and one's sequencing budget, typically one or more of the following three main metagenome sequencing strategies could be taken. Here we only see an overview of the experimental technology, but we will expand the analysis tasks for each in later chapters.

1.3.1 *Targeted amplicon sequencing*

Targeted amplicon sequencing (TAS) strategy offers a rapid and affordable way to determine what species are present and their relative abundance, by sequencing only one gene, or a specific region of a gene of each microbial species. It was the method of choice to profile a metagenome before the year 2010 due to its low sequencing cost. Although the genes being targeted can vary depending on the scientific questions, the genes encoding the 16S/18S small subunit of the ribosome (SSU) are most commonly chosen as a proxy for bacterial/archaeal and eukaryotic genomes, respectively. PCR experiments amplify the variable regions of the SSU gene and the amplicons are subsequently sequenced. The sequenced SSU genes/regions can be relatively easily analyzed to obtain each species' abundance that constitutes the community structure, or to construct phylogenetic trees to infer community composition. We will discuss TAS-based computational analysis in detail in Chapter 6.

TAS sequencing is analogous to a census of microbes, by cataloging a rough estimate of what species are present at what abundance in a community. It can be quite sensitive, revealing rare members that exist in only a few copies. It is, however, not a comprehensive survey. For example, it does not catalog viruses, which do not carry their own SSU genes. Nor does it survey species with less conserved SSU genes/regions where the PCR primers recognize. Moreover, errors introduced by PCR amplification such as point mutations (base substitutions, insertions/deletions) and chimeras may lead to spurious species that do not actually exist.

1.3.2 *Whole metagenome sequencing*

Besides surveying microbial diversity, another motivation that we study metagenomics is to comprehensively discover novel species including viruses, and novel candidate genes or pathways with desired metabolic capabilities such as secondary metabolism that microbes invented but proven extremely useful for our medicine. For these purposes, we turn to the most commonly used strategy for metagenome sequencing today, Whole Metagenome (shotgun) Sequencing (WGS or WMGS). With this strategy, we first collect the genomic DNA from a metagenomic sample and then shear it randomly into small pieces (this is why it is called shotgun sequencing). Each piece is then sequenced using massively parallel sequencing technology and digitally transformed into a read (Figure 1.1). Breaking metagenomic DNA into short pieces is necessary to achieve high-throughput sequencing and to accommodate the read length limitation of current sequencers (see next section). To ensure no part of the genome is omitted by random sampling, or to have a good sequencing coverage, and to ensure random sequence errors are corrected, each position of the genome is sequenced more than once, sometimes by thousands of times (sequencing depth). These reads are then computationally assembled into genes or genomes for further analysis. WGS is less biased against novel species than TAS, and yet rivals its sensitivity to detect rare

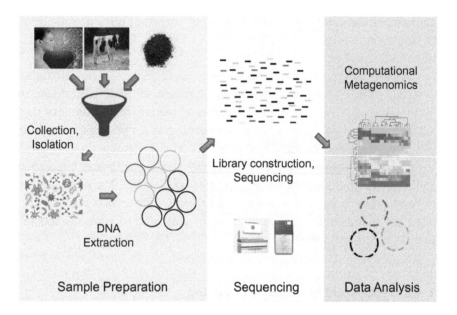

Fig. 1.1   An overview of a whole metagenome sequencing project. A typical project consists of three phases. In the sample preparation phase, samples are collected from various environments, and microbial materials are separated from the rest, followed by a DNA extraction step to harvest metagenomic DNA. In the sequencing phase, metagenomic DNA is sheared into small pieces and made into sequencing libraries. The libraries are then sequenced by the high-throughput sequencers to obtain sequencing data. The data is then analyzed in the data analysis phase, using strategies and techniques covered in this book.

species given sufficient sequencing, therefore it is replacing TAS for surveying diversity. Having genomic sequences of the microbes also unlocks the ability to predict their metabolism capacity and even their interaction.

WGS creates substantial challenges for downstream analysis, as computational biologists are faced with both a data challenge and an algorithmic one, let alone that it can be quite costly experimentally and computationally. A single WGS metagenomic dataset could reach terabases of sequences with trillions of reads. Metagenome assembly, the process to piece together these pieces into genomes, requires software tools that are both scalable and accurate. WGS-based computational analysis is the focus of this book, as you will see in later chapters.

1.3.3 *Single-cell amplification genome sequencing*

Unlike WGS metagenome sequencing that tackles the whole community at once, single-cell amplification genome sequencing (SAGS) adopts a "divide-and-conquer" strategy. With this strategy, we first isolate single cells using the state-of-art droplet-based liquid handling techniques, then process their DNA in parallel (extract genomic DNA, amplify it, and add a barcode), and finally combine the resulting barcoded fragments for sequencing. Unlike in TAS that employs PCR to amplify only a certain region of the genome, in SAGS, the whole genome is amplified using a rolling circle amplification approach (RCA).

SAGS introduces significant technical hurdles in preparing sequencing libraries to gain an advantage in reducing downstream computational complexity. It is one of the most rapidly developing areas in metagenomics. With a sufficient number of species covered, we can obtain community diversity and structure as in TAS and WGS. When enough cells from a species are sequenced, we not only can get a complete genome of this species but also can understand individual genome variations within this species that are not possible with other strategies. We will discuss SAGS-based computational analysis in greater detail in Chapter 9.

Table 1.1 provides a brief review of the three sequencing strategies we just covered.

Table 1.1   The three sequencing strategies.

	Targeted Amplicon Sequencing (TAS)	Whole Genome Shotgun (WGS)	Single-cell Amplification Genome Sequencing (SAGS)
Sequencing Targets	16S/18S	Metagenome	Multiple genomes
Amplification/Method	Yes/PCR	Maybe/PCR	Yes/ RCA
Technical Challenge	Low	Low	High
Data Analysis Complexity	Low	Very High	High
Recover Single Genomes?	No	Maybe	Maybe
Cost	Low	High	High
Applications	Diversity	Diversity, function	Function, variation

1.4 Metagenome Sequencing: Platforms

Thanks to the revolution of DNA sequencing technologies in the past decade, we are now blessed with several sequencing platforms to interrogate complex microbial communities. An understanding of these sequencing technologies is a prerequisite for effective data analysis as data from each platform carries unique characteristics. Here let us take a brief overview of the current next-generation sequencing technology platforms.

1.4.1 *Illumina*

Sequencing technology developed by Illumina is the predominant next-generation sequencing technology. Genomic DNA or its amplified derivatives are first fragmented, and adapters are added to each fragment to make sequencing libraries. The resulting libraries are then sequenced in a massively parallel fashion, resulting in millions to billions of short sequences (reads) of length 100–300 bases. The sequencing is done by first synthesizing a new strand using the library DNA as a template, where fluorescently labeled deoxyribonucleoside triphosphates (dNTPs) are incorporated and "read" by image analysis one by one after their incorporation. This type of sequencing is called "sequencing by synthesis". Even though the sequencing process is done in a base-by-base cycle (synthesis, imagining, removing fluorescence labels) and is stopped after 150 cycles, sequencing throughput is achieved by simultaneously sequencing billions of short read templates. More often, the DNA templates are sequenced from both ends to obtain a read pair, thus effectively reading 300 bases per fragment. Sequencing errors could be introduced during the synthesis or image analysis steps, but in general at a very low rate (1–2%). More details can be found on the company's website: https://www.illumina.com/science/technology/next-generation-sequencing/beginners.html#how-it-works

Illumina sequencers each generate an enormous amount of data in a single run, ranging from 120 gigabases (gigabase is a billion base, or 10^9 base) to 6,000 gigabases. Because of its low cost and high throughput nature, the majority of the available metagenomic data are from Illumina as of today.

1.4.2 *Pacific Biosciences*

In the above Illumina sequencing, each DNA fragment was first amplified a few hundreds of times to form a "cluster", or a clone of the
original fragment, so that the fluorescent signal from a cluster is
more robust than that from a single molecule. The sequencing technology developed by Pacific Biosciences Inc (PacBio), in contrast,
is a single-molecule, real-time sequencing strategy. PacBio sequencing uses large DNA molecules as templates, each undergoing an
independent sequencing-by-synthesis process that is captured opti-
cally into a real-time movie. Signals contained in these movies are
then analyzed to predict the underlying DNA sequences. Because
the sequencing reaction is observed in real-time instead of going
through sequencing cycles, PacBio sequencing reads are much longer,
up to 30 kb, one of the biggest advantages of this strategy. Because
single-molecule sequencing has a low signal-to-noise ratio, PacBio
sequencing has much higher error rates (15%), predominantly inser-
tion/deletion errors. More details are available at https://www.pacb.
com/smrt-science/smrt-sequencing/.

The long read length greatly reduces the genome assembly complexity, resulting in the rapid adoption of PacBio sequencing in single
genome assembly projects. Its adoption in metagenome sequencing,
however, is hindered by the relative high error rates and higher costs
of early generations of PacBio sequencers.

1.4.3 *Oxford Nanopore Technology*

Both Illumina and PacBio are using sequencing-by-synthesis techniques, where DNA polymerases are employed to read the metagenomic DNA libraries. The nanopore sequencing technology (ONT)
developed by Oxford Nanopore Inc is completely different. In ONT
sequencing, a strand of DNA (which is negatively charged) is driven
by an electric current to pass through a protein pore on a membrane.
The current changes, caused by the blockage of different bases passing through the pore, are captured and interpreted into sequences.
(https://nanoporetech.com/how-it-works). ONT also has a long-read
advantage and high error rate disadvantage as PacBio. One of its
sequencers, the MinION, unlike the other sequencers that weigh in

Table 1.2   Three sequencing platforms to interrogate complex microbial communities.

	Illumina	Pacific Biosciences (PacBio)	Oxford Nanopore (ONT)
Read length	150–300	1000–30,000	500–100,000
Single-molecule Sequencing?	No	Yes	Yes
Throughput	Very high	High	High
Cost	Low	High	High
Error rate	1–2%	15%	10%?
Data from a single run	120 Gb (NextSeq 550) 300 Gb (NextSeq 2000) 6,000 Gb (NovaSeq 6000)	20 Gb (Sequel)	10–20 Gb (MinION) 7,600 Gb (PromethION-48)
Applications	Amplicon, WGS, SAGS	WGS	WGS

Data Source:
1. https://www.illumina.com/systems/sequencing-platforms.html
2. https://www.pacb.com/products-and-services/sequel-system/
3. https://nanoporetech.com/products

tons, weighs in grams and has the size of a USB drive. This portable sequencer has been used in remote locations such as the International Space Station (Nicholas *et al.*, 2017).

As PacBio sequencing, ONT has not been broadly adopted in metagenome sequencing. ONT's PromethION-48 platform can rival the largest Illumina sequencers for throughput, producing 7,600 gigabases in a single run, which has the potential to sequence the most complex microbial communities.

Table 1.2 provides a brief review of the three sequencing platforms we just discussed.

1.4.4 *Emerging technologies*

For metagenome sequencing, we are caught in a dilemma between high-throughput, accurate but shorter reads offered by Illumina, and low-throughput, inaccurate but longer reads offered by PacBio and ONT. Could we have the benefits of both worlds?

Assuming the errors are random, one strategy is to sequence the same DNA molecule multiple times to increase accuracy. The following

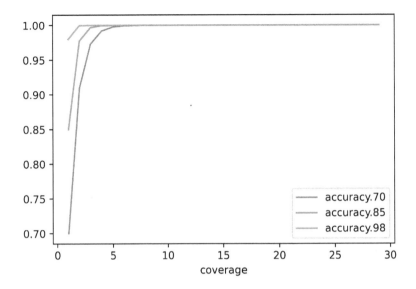

Fig. 1.2 Sequencing coverage vs base accuracy at different error rates.

plot helps to illustrate this point. For Nanopore-1D (70% accuracy), PacBio (85% accuracy), and Illumina (98% accuracy), if we have 5 or more reads that cover the same base, the accuracy is close to 100% (Figure 1.2). PacBio's latest technology uses the circular consensus sequencing (CCS) mode that sequences the same molecule multiple times, a consensus sequence can then be derived with a base accuracy over >99.5% (Wenger *et al.*, 2019). ONT sequencing can also make both strands of the DNA pass the nanopore to reduce errors (2-D sequencing). These high-fidelity versions, becoming less expensive with improved throughput, could enable their rapid adoption in metagenome sequencing.

Another strategy is to use short reads to "synthesize" long reads. These technologies, sometimes also called "read clouds" or "linked reads", first partition one or a few large genomic fragments into a liquid droplet, where a mini short read library with a unique barcode is generated. Each mini-library represents a "cloud" of reads originating from a long fragment in the same droplet, or in other words, these reads are "linked" by the barcode. The resulting mini-libraries are then combined and sequenced using the Illumina platform, and the reads from each large molecule can be separated based on their barcodes and assembled. The assembly process is much more simplified as it only has to deal with a few segments at a time, as opposed to the entire metagenome. The assembled large fragments can then be further assembled to reconstruct the metagenome.

Current sequencing technology continues evolving to bring longer reads, reduced cost, and higher sequencing accuracy. Combining Internet of Things (IoT) and edge computing, future sequencing technologies may enable "edge metagenome sequencing" directly from various habitats, or sequencing is done on portable sequencers (such as an ONT MinION) and data is sent directly to the cloud. This would be particular important for metagenomics, as currently we do not have a technology to monitor a microbial community in real time. To prevent another global pandemic, such technology would allow us to quickly identify a new pathogen, or a new strain of a known pathogen that is responsible for an emerging infectious disease. Miniaturized automatic sequencers as sensors would be essential for real-time surveillance of the evolution of viruses in the wild.

1.5　Metagenomics: A Great Promise with Abundant Caution

Fueled by the recent development of sequencing technology and big data analytic, our understanding of the microbiome is on steroids. Numerous correlations have been established between specific microbes or microbiome dynamics and a wide range of phenotypes that include disease, responses to therapy, and environmental changes. These potentially important correlations have led laboratories around the world to explore the mechanisms that could establish causal links between specific microbes and a phenotype. It is easy for us to imagine that in the near future we will be able to digitally isolate each individual microbe in a complex environment, tease out its intricate genetic secrets for adaptation, and predict its rise and fall with environmental changes. However, here I would like to spell a few words of caution.

First of all, getting the sequence of a microbial genome is a rather a new beginning, rather than an end. Genomics sequencing alone is a poor predictor of the phenotype of a microbe. We would need to combine it with metadata, or the environmental context the microbe is living within, to further understand the potential encoded in its genome. We could construct a metabolic map containing various predicted metabolic pathways from the genome, but these pathways tell little about the physiology, metabolism, and habitat this organism can adapt to. Too many published papers make too many speculations based solely on metagenomic data. We need additional data, particularly function data such as transcriptomic, proteomic, metabolic, and physiologic data to faithfully interpret genome sequence data. Of course, obtaining these data takes greater effort and cost, and this explains why they are often missing from the study. Conclusions from a metagenomics study with only genomics data should be always taken with a grain of salt.

Second, despite the fact that we have studied quite a few genes and genomes, it is likely that what we have only sampled a tiny fraction of the diversity of the microbial world. Even as one of the bacteria we know best, *Escherichia coli* still has about 17% of its proteins with unknown functions and 34.6% of genes lack experimental evidence of function (Ghatak *et al.*, 2019). Every new genome we reconstructed from the environment contains many more unknown proteins, some genomes may be close to unrecognisable with few known genes. Just like microbiology has a skewed representation by only a few pathogens (*E. coli*, Salmonella, etc), current metagenomics is also heavily biased towards the human microbiome as a subject.

Finally, the technologies employed in metagenomics all have biases, gaps, noises, and other limits. For example, as other omics studies, we may never get to 100% completeness. We may miss rare species, which turns out to play vital roles in the community. These rare species are actually much harder to get to, because it takes an increasing amount of sequencing to see them, if we can distinguish them from noise.

Chapter 2

Computational Metagenomics: A Data Engineering Perspective

Last decade marks a few events for the dawn of a big data era. Founded at 2005, YouTube reaches 2.3 billion monthly active users worldwide as of 2021 and hosts 720,000 hours of video uploaded every day (https://www.oberlo.com/blog/youtube-statistics). Twitter, created in 2006, now has 192 million daily active users and they send out more than half a billion tweets each day (https://www.oberlo.com/blog/twitter-statistics). The genomics big data era also started around the same time frame. In 2005, the Sequencing-By-Synthesis technology from a UK startup, Solexa, delivered over 3 million bases from a single sequencing run to obtain the complete genome of bacteriophage phiX-174. The next year, the first Solexa sequencer was launched with the power to sequence 1 gigabase (Gb) of data in a single run. While Youtube and Twitter have long passed their exponential growth stage, the rate of increase in sequencing data is still growing exponentially, and it has far surpassed the rate predicted by Moore's law (Figure 2.1). The number of nucleotide base pairs (bp) in public repositories is estimated to reach exabase-scale (10^{18} bp) before 2025 (Stephens et al., 2015). Metagenomics data is one of the largest contributors to this data growth.

Today's metagenomics has largely become a data science problem, as data generation has increasingly become a smaller part. Back to the planning trip analogy I made at the beginning of the book, the data is both cargo and fuel. The cargo aspect of data means they are a burden

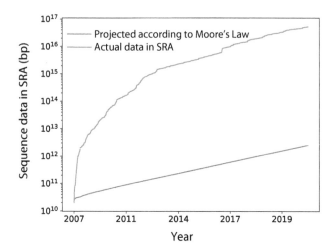

Fig. 2.1 Sequence data growth in the National Center for Biotechnology Information (NCBI) Short read archive (SRA) vs a hypothetical rate predicted by Moore's Law (doubling every two years).
Data source: https://trace.ncbi.nlm.nih.gov/Traces/sra/sra_stat.cgi

on our computational metagenomics task, and larger data means a heavier burden. The fuel aspect of data means they contain valuable information for data mining engines, as more data translates into better machine learning models.

In this chapter, we will get to know the various data types in computational metagenomics, what are their specific applications, and the strategies to effectively manage them. I will discuss computer algorithms to process them in the next chapter, while leaving the discussion of scalable big data analytics to Chapter 4.

2.1 An Overview of Metagenomics Data Management

Historically, genomics data used to be scarce. In the first generation sequencing era dominated by Sanger sequencing, a good data management practice was to save every bit of data we generated, as data generation was expensive at that time. We would make several copies of the data so that accidentally losing one copy would not be consequential. We would submit it along with the associated analysis results to online databases so that everyone in the world can print them out and make more copies. One person can easily do the whole process. We seldom need to wait for hours or days to transfer our data, even though our hard drives and internet connections were slow and unreliable at that time. In the next-generation sequencing era with large data volumes and various data formats, however, this *ad hoc* data management strategy will no doubt fail us. An individual is no longer able to be responsible for data backup, versioning, and sharing. Even with a dedicated data management team, many institutions are struggling to come up with an effective data management strategy as data volume grows exponentially and their formats constantly evolve. The rapid development of analytical tools also exacerbates the data management problem by creating more formats and versions. The prevalence of applying next-generation sequencing to medical fields also makes the security and privacy problem bigger to handle.

There may not exist a perfect data management strategy, but we know a good data strategy should be defined by the underlying scientific or business goals. For large organizations, a good strategy should also consider a dedicated team led by a genomics data architect. Here, I will assume that readers are more interested in data management at the project level in a small team setting. The same principles could also be applied when we need to scale up.

When we talk about metagenomic data management, there are three aspects we have to consider: information, storage, and governance (Figure 2.2). From a metagenomics perspective, what kind of information do we need to capture? For a typical metagenomics project, we capture sequencing data as well as the metadata that describes how the experiments are carried out. From a data engineering perspective, after these information are captured, where and how should we store them? What file formats will be efficient for our downstream analytic tasks from an algorithmic perspective? What database system should we use to organize our data? What format will incur smaller costs? What information should we keep secure and private? While the questions do not stop here, I will walk you through these aspects of data management, starting from the types of data to capture metagenomics information, followed by data governance (database systems), and finally the consideration of storage and process choices.

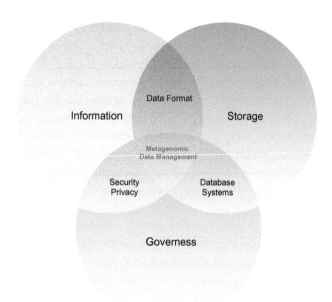

Fig. 2.2   Considerations for metagenomics data management.

2.2 Types of Data in Metagenomics

It seems that there are countless types of data in the world of data science, and people are still inventing new ones. The data taxonomy itself is messy. It is easier to understand these data types if we look at the three pillars of computational metagenomics introduced in the first chapter, i.e, look at them in the context of metagenomics, data engineering, and algorithms, respectively. The metagenomics context deals with what information to capture and store to serve the scientific problem at hand, the data engineering context deals with how to represent this information efficiently given the computing infrastructure at hand, while the algorithm context deals with how to organize this information for faster (or approximate) solutions.

2.2.1 *Data types in the context of metagenomics*

In the context of metagenomics, we have omics (genomics, transcriptomics, proteomics, or metabolomics) data. These data types are named after specific scientific questions or specific experimental technologies that produce them. There is also metadata, or data describing the details of the experiment from which our omics data derive. Metadata of environmental samples often include where and when they are collected, such as longitude and latitude, and some physiochemical descriptions of the samples such as PH, humidity, and temperature. The metadata of clinical samples often includes descriptions of the patients such as gender, age, smoke/alcohol/antibiotic usage history. We often collect as much metadata as possible, in various formats, voluntarily or demanded by online repositories. Here I limit our discussion to DNA sequences only, as we will mention other formats in later chapters when we discuss specific software tools. I will introduce a few common data formats, and a comprehensive guide of next-generation sequence data formats can be found at The National Center for Biotechnology Information (NCBI) website: https://www.ncbi.nlm.nih.gov/sra/docs/submitformats/.

2.2.1.1 *DNA sequence data*

Regardless of what sequencers generate our sequence data, we need to capture at least three types of information: 1) the DNA sequence itself; 2) as we mentioned in Chapter 1 sequencers have various error rates, for each of the recorded sequenced bases we need the associated probability of it being correct; and 3) some metadata about the source of the sequence data and how they are generated.

FastQ

FastQ format is one of the most common sequence formats produced by the next-generation sequencers. It records the ID, sequence, and quality of a read. ID provides a unique identification of a read. It could also contain some metadata information, albeit very limited. For example, in a FastQ file generated by Illumina platform, the sequence ID contains the machine type, flow cell information, coordinates of the flow cell, read pair information, and barcodes, etc. Each sequence record consists of four lines: an ID line begins with an extra "@", the sequence line, another ID line begins with an extra "+", and finally the line of quality scores. The second ID is often omitted as it is identical to the first one. The PHRED quality score (integers between 0 and 90) is a nonnegative quality value of each called base. It is the log-transformed error probability,

$$Q = -10 * log10(Pe) \tag{1}$$

In FastQ files, we actually do not represent quality scores as a numerical format. Instead, they are encoded into a compact format so that each quality score uses only 1 byte. In this encoding, the quality score is represented as a character with an ASCII code equal to its value +33. The following table demonstrates the relationship between the error probability, its corresponding PHRED score, and its encoded character:

```
Error prob.    PHRED Score      FastQ Encoding
Pe = 1.0       Q =  0           !
Pe = 0.1       Q = 10           +
Pe = 0.01      Q = 20           5
Pe = 0.001     Q = 30           ?
Pe = 0.001     Q = 40           I
```

The FastQ formatted files have extensions "fastq" or "fq". As a plain text, it is easy for humans to read but very inefficient for storage, so in practice they are compressed by gzip, resulting in "fq.gz" as their file extension.

The following are two read examples from FastQ files, the first one is a pair of short reads derived from Illumina sequencing, the second one is a single read from PacBio sequencing.

A read pair sequenced by Illumina NovoSeq, the sequence ID line follows this format: @<instrument>:<run number>:<flowcell ID>:<lane>:<tile>:<x-pos>:<y-pos> <read>:<is filtered>:<control number>:<sample number>. More information can be found at https://help.basespace.illumina.com/articles/descriptive/fastq-files/.

```
@HISEQ09:412:CBT0RANXX:5:1114:15323:37302 1:N:0:TAGCTT
ACAATAAATATTATTATCTTCATCAATTTTTTTTTTTTTGTTTTAGTTTTTGTTTTTTTTTTTTTTTTTTTGGTTTTTTTTTTTTTTT
TTTTTTTTTTTTTTTTTTTTTAAAATTATTAATTTTTTTATTATTTTTTTTTTTTTTTTTTTTTTTTT
+HISEQ09:412:CBT0RANXX:5:1114:15323:37302 1:N:0:TAGCTT
CCCCCGGGGGGGGGGGGGGGGGGGGGGGGGGGGGGGGGGGGGGGGGGGGDGEED>CEDFG/FGGGGGGGGGGGGG/C////::DGGGGGB///ED
GGGGGGGGGG#######################################################
@HISEQ09:412:CBT0RANXX:5:1114:15323:37302 2:N:0:TAGCTT
ATATTCAATAAATAAAAAAAAAAAAAAAAACGTACAAAAAAAAAAAAAAAAATAAAAAAAAAAAAATTAAAAAAATAAAAAAAAAAA
AAAAAATTTTTGAAAAATTTTTTTTTTTTTAAAAAATAATAAAAAAAAAAAAAAAAAAAAAAAAAAAA
+HISEQ09:412:CBT0RANXX:5:1114:15323:37302 2:N:0:TAGCTT
<3<001@E1@FG1@FGGG/EEGG//<EG//110=FGGGGGGGGGGGGGA/09;0DGG/:CGG;/00;;9C@:/099DGECG//..
...6.../////..///C.66//.......//6/..8//68DDGGGGGDGGG..CGGGGGGGDG###
```

A read derived from the PacBio Sequel II system. In this specific example, the ID line follows this format: @m_<Time of Run Start (yymmdd_hhmmss)>/<Instrument Serial Number>/<Subread Region (start_stop>.

```
@m64021_191003_193626/4/0_3252
ACGAAACGTCCCTCTTAACGACCGCGACCGGACATTCCTACTTCGCCGGAGCACATAAATGGAATGCTTTGAAATGTAAGTCGA
TTCGCGTCCCGGAGTGACTGGAGTTGACTCTCGCGCTGGGGCGGGCAAAAGAAAGGTGGTCGAG
(many more lines are skipped)
GGAGGGGGGGGGGGTGGGGGGGGGGTGGGGGCAATAAGTGACAGTTGCGAGTCTGTTACGCCAGCGAGCCTGGGAATGGGGGGG
GGGAAGCCGTAAGAAGGGGGCGGTGGGGAGCGGGTGGAGGGGGGGGGGGGGGGGCCACCCGAACA
+
########################################################################
################################################################
(many more lines are skipped)
########################################################################
################################################################
```

FastA

In cases where sequencing quality is not important or not relevant, sequences are stored in FastA format. Most reference genomes are stored in FastA format, as their quality is presumed to be very high. The FastA formatted files have extensions "fasta" or "fa". As for FastQ, FastA files are also plain text files, and they are often compressed to have extensions such as "fa.gz". The following example is a representation of the first sequence in the above FastQ example in FastA format.

```
>HISEQ09:412:CBT0RANXX:5:1114:15323:37302 1:N:0:TAGCTT
ACAATAAATATTATTATCTTCATCAATTTTTTTTTTTTGTTTTAGTTTTGTTTTTTTTTTTTTTTTTTTGGTTTTTTTTTTTTTT
TTTTTTTTTTTTTTTTTTTTAAAATTATTAATTTTTTTATTATTTTTTTTTTTTTTTTTTTTTTTTTT
```

SAM/BAM

If there is a reference available, the sequence data can also be represented in Sequence Alignment/Mapping (SAM) format. A reference could be a set of known reference genomes of the species in the microbial community where the raw sequences are derived. It could also be a metagenome reference assembled from the reads (see Chapter 8 for metagenome assembly). SAM format is produced by mapping the sequence reads to the reference to determine the location of each read on the reference. It contains all information in a FastQ file, and in addition it contains mapping information (the location of the reference genome and the quality of the mapping). SAM format and its binary equivalent, BAM, are widely used in software tools developed for next-generation data. We will see its application frequently in later chapters. A complete specification of SAM/BAM format can be found here: https://samtools.github.io/hts-specs/SAMv1.pdf. SAM/BAM files can be sorted and indexed for fast random access. A SAM/BAM file consists of two parts, a header portion that describes metadata (the reference and how the mapping is done), and a data portion that contains the mapping information.

Below is an example of a SAM/BAM file. For illustration purposes, it only shows two reference sequences and two reads, the first read is mapped while the second one is not:

```
@HD VN:1.4  SO:unsorted
@SQ SN:NODE_2_length_815_cov_8.922368    LN:815
@SQ SN:NODE_1922_length_105_cov_1.460000    LN:105
HISEQ09:412:CBT0RANXX:5:1311:6356:89265 2:N:0:TAGCTT    16  NODE_1922_length_105_cov_1.460000    1
152S105=23S    *  0  0  TTCCTTTTCCTTTTCCTTTTCCTTTTCCTTTTTCCTTTTTCCTTTTTTCCTTTTTTCCTTTTTCC
TTTTTTTCCTTTTTTCCTTTTTTCCTTTTTTCCTTTTTTCCTTTTTTCCTTTTTTCCTTTTTCCTTTTTT    <@BGGGGBBGEB@8.8.=G@.GGGGGC>G<@E
EEDGC6GEEGGGGED=GGB>AGBGGGDDBGD@GGBGGGGGGGGGGGGGGGGGGGGGGGDFGFB<GEGDGC/GFGGGGGDGGFGGGGGGGGGGGGGEGGGGGGGGGGGGGGGGGFGGGGBCBB
@B   NM:i:0  AM:i:15
HISEQ09:412:CBT0RANXX:5:1302:17219:76080 2:N:0:TAGCTT    4   *  0  0  *  *  0
0   CAAAAAAAAACCAAAACAACTCTTCCTTATGCGTATCATTGGATAAAGCTCTTTCTAGGTGTAACTCGACGCCACCAAACATAGGTTAAGGGGAGCCTTGAGTATTCGCCT
TTGTTCTTCCCCCATGGGTAACGCATGCGACCATAAAA  <AB000=/E//</00<E1:0C=B1BFGGD11E1F<=/:DG:FGC>DCGF1:111:>FGGG>EGGGG0<BBGGB>/F
GGGGGEEG08;DGC00......./9:/6:@//8.6>>/D6DEGDDEGGGGG;.@BGGBGGGGG=@DD,>GGGGE
```

2.2.1.2 *Annotation data*

Another common type of genomics data is annotation data. Annotation data describes the taxonomy or function of the genetic elements (genes, transcripts, etc) or genetic features (repeats, promoters, variants, etc). Common annotation file types include GFF (General Feature Format) and BED (BED (Browser Extensible Data). People in the clinical genomics and population genomics fields also use VCF (Variant Call Format) to annotate mutations/variants. In metagenomics, VCF has not been widely adopted, reflecting this field is relatively young. We will take a glimpse at the GFF and BED formats below.

GFF3

GFF format is specified by the GMOD project (http://gmod.org/wiki/Main_Page). GFF format consists of one line per feature, each containing 9 columns of data, plus optional track definition lines. The following example is based on the Version 3 specifications from the GMOD website, describing the annotation of a transcript, mrna0001 on chromosome ctg123.

```
##gff-version 3
ctg123 . mRNA       1300  9000  .  +  .   ID=mrna0001;Name=transcript1
ctg123 . exon       1300  1500  .  +  .   ID=exon00001;Parent=mrna0001
ctg123 . exon       1050  1500  .  +  .   ID=exon00002;Parent=mrna0001
ctg123 . exon       3000  3902  .  +  .   ID=exon00003;Parent=mrna0001
ctg123 . exon       5000  5500  .  +  .   ID=exon00004;Parent=mrna0001
ctg123 . exon       7000  9000  .  +  .   ID=exon00005;Parent=mrna0001
```

It is worth noting that in the process of capturing experimental information, the above data formats discussed above were designed for humans to read. In the big data era, these data types are neither space efficient nor easy to access. We will discuss these issues later in this chapter.

BED

BED format is specified by UCSC Genome Browser community (https://genome.ucsc.edu/FAQ/FAQformat.html#format1). It provides a flexible way to define and display annotations. The above GFF format can be converted to the following BED format:

```
track name=exampleBED description="An example of BED" useScore=1
ctg123 1300 9000 mrna0001 1000 + 1000 9000 255,0,0 2 1300,1050,3000,5000,7000 1500,
1500m3902,5500,9000
```

2.2.1.3 Metadata

From experiment design, sample collection, sequencing to data analysis, each of the steps in the life cycle of a metagenomics project produces metadata that describes the sequence data and annotation data we discussed earlier. These metadata contain important information for understanding genomic data. The earliest metadata were handwritten notes, and they later evolved into spread sheets. Researchers soon realized that it was painful not to have common standards for sharing and exchange of such data. In 2005, the Genomic Standards Consortium (GSC) initiative was formed including several sequencing centers (NCBI, EMBL, DDBJ, JCVI, JGI, EBI, Sanger, FIG) to standardize the description of (meta)genomes. GSC specified the MIMS standard, which stands for Minimum Information about any

Table 2.1   Metadata describing a user.

Name	Value
acct_id	**0000**
acct_purpose	Programmatic
acct_scientific_program	Metagenome
acct_user_program	A JGI Partner
acct_year	2020

Metagenome Sequence, for metagenome metadata (https://gensc.org/). Without going much detail into the MIMS standard, I will use some mock examples from JGI to illustrate how metadata is recorded.

As JGI is a user facility, the metadata describing a user is shown in Table 2.1.

After JGI is committed to support a user's research proposal, the proposal information metadata is captured by a Table 2.2: "Scientific proposal information".

The metadata describing the genomic sequencing itself, including information about the sequencing library and sequencing platform, is shown in Table 2.3: "Sequencing metrics".

JGI's analysis pipelines produce metadata like those shown in Table 2.4: "Analysis summary".

The above tables just captured a tiny portion of the various metadata associated with a metagenomics project. Like the metagenome sequence itself, the size and variety of metadata are also getting bigger. Next, we will explore data types from data engineering and algorithmic contexts, to learn how to represent these data and how to process them efficiently.

Table 2.2   Scientific proposal information.

Name	Value
proposal_id	506431
proposal_pi	Doe, John
proposal_title	The purpose of this proposal is to study a problem of highly relevant to DOE missions

Table 2.3   Sequencing metrics.

Name	Value
sow_item_type	Fragment
sow_lib_creation_specs	Illumina Regular Fragment, 270bp
sow_lib_protocol	Regular (DNA)
sow_logical_amt_unit	Gb
sow_overlap_reads	N
sow_platform	Illumina
sow_poly_a_selection	N
sow_prev_status	Awaiting Collaborator Metadata
sow_purpose	Anticipated Planned Work
sow_rrna_depletion	N
sow_seq_model	NovaSeq S4
sow_status	Awaiting Collaborator Metadata
sow_target_dop	60
sow_target_logical_amt	11
sow_target_mass_lib_trial_ng	100
sow_target_run_type	2×150
sow_target_template_size_bp	270
sow_tight_insert	N

Table 2.4   Analysis summary.

Name	Value
sp_actual_product	Metagenome Minimal Draft
sp_actual_sam_map_strategy	1:All
sp_auto_sched_sow_items	N
sp_comments	10 Gb

2.2.2   *Data types in the context of data engineering*

We just went over what information to capture and store (metagenomics context), now let us see how these information can be represented and organized. In the context of data engineering, data can be represented as textual, numerical, or binary types. Each of these types of data can also adopt different formats. When choosing a data format, a data engineer has to balance storage and access efficiency and makes a compromise if a trade-off is involved. To make data storage efficient, we want to keep as little redundancy as possible, reducing both data and information redundancy. To make data access efficient, we want to have the ability to quickly sample or slice portions of the data without first going through the entire body of data. The reason for efficiently sampling data is two folds: the first reason is that we may not be able to load all data in memory for analysis as many are too big to fit in; the second reason, for some of the scientific questions such as evaluating data quality and estimating community richness, is that we often do not need all data to be able to answer them.

2.2.2.1 *CSV and JSON*

For textual and numerical data, there are two predominant formats, CSV and JSON, across many scientific domains. CSV, or comma-separated values (sometimes tabs are used to separate values, hence TSV), is the most common format to store textual or numerical data in a tabular format. FastQ, FastA, GFF3, and BED data formats we discussed earlier are essentially variants of TSV format, and they can be easily transformed into TSV format.

JavaScript Object Notation (JSON) provides an easily readable format by maintaining a dictionary-style structure. JSON is a versatile and flexible data format in the context of web interactions. Metagenomics data analysis services such as NCBI and MG-RAST (https://www.mg-rast.org/), use RESTful APIs to provide access to their data and analysis results by answering web queries with structured JSON data. JSON format is the format of choice for metadata, as an example, the previous user and proposal metadata can be represented as the following JSON format.

```
{
    "user_info": [
        "acct_id": "0000",
        "acct_purpose": "Programmatic",
        "acct_scientific_program": "Metagenome",
        "acct_user_program": "A JGI Partner",
        "acct_year": 2020
    ],
    "Scientific proposal information": [
        "proposal_id": 506431,
        "proposal_pi": "Doe, John",
        "proposal_title": "The purpose of this proposal
        is to study a problem highly relevant to DOE missions"
    ]
}
```

Both CSV and JSON formats are easy for humans to read, write, and interpret. However, these formats are not space-efficient, neither are they easy to access when files become very large. To improve their space efficiency, they are often stored in compressed format on the storage system. On Linux systems, gzip or tar.gz are the two most common formats for compression. Compression unfortunately makes the accessible problems worse, as the files may have to be decompressed before some software tools can analyze them. Another problem is that data in these formats can only be accessed sequentially, much like songs stored on a tape, we would have to read and skip all data before reaching the data we want. For random access of data, we would need databases.

2.2.2.2 *Databases*

CSV and JSON formatted data can be stored in databases, where data records are indexed to enable random access. There are two types of databases: the traditional relational database and the new NoSQL database. A Relational Database Management System (RDMS) stores information as a series of related data tables. The vast majority of the databases used in metagenomics are relational databases. The metadata tables we saw earlier are all part of JGI's metadata database. These tables have a fixed schema (a.k.a. structure), and the information stored in these tables can be queried using SQL (Structured Query Language). RDMS provides good performance when the data is relatively small, but their performance degrades quickly as the data gets bigger. For example, for a database table with billions of rows, adding a new attribute to a single row would require billions of operations as a new column is added to the entire table.

NoSQL databases are also referred as document databases. Instead of storing related tables with structured data, they store data in key-value pairs or JSON documents that are unstructured or semistructured. As Relational databases, NoSQL databases also index data for random access. Unlike Relational databases, the flexible schema of NoSQL allows adding/removing attributes with ease. NoSQL is the format of choice for storing big data as it offers high scalability, resilience, and high availability (by default, data is replicated in multiple copies). Readers can learn more about NoSQL from leading vendors such as MongoDB (https://www.mongodb.com/nosql-explained). A variant of NoSQL, NoSQL Graph database, that is very promising to model the complex relationships among metagenomics knowledge, such as metabolic networks, phylogenetic relationships, and interspecies interactions. By representing relationships in native graph format, graph databases bring effective relationship mining to big data.

2.2.2.3 *HDF5*

For storage and access performance reasons, most data management systems store sequence data in compressed CSV/JSON format since they do not need random access, while storing structured metadata in various databases for rapid information retrieval. There is a risk of potential disconnection between the two, for example, the record of a sequence file path in a database is accidentally modified, or the sequence file itself is unintentionally moved without updating its corresponding record.

The Hierarchical Data Format version 5 (HDF5) solves the above problem. It is an open-source file format that supports heterogeneous data types. An HDF5 file is rather a "container", as it organizes all data, both sequence and meta-data, related to an experiment in a structured way. It supports compression and slicing, which makes it both efficient in storage and data access. It also has Application Programming Interfaces (APIs) that support many programming languages, including Python and R. The ability to embed metadata inside the file makes HDF5 self-describing, which facilitates data sharing and downstream processing. Both PacBio and Nanopore raw sequencing data formats are in HDF5 format. The metagenomics community has made a derivative of HDF5 by creating the BIOM file format, designed to be a general-use format for representing biological samples. BIOM is a recognized standard by the Earth Microbiome Project and the Genomics Standards Consortium (https://biom-format.org/). The following are the required top-level attributes defined in BIOM v2.1:

```
id          : <string or null> field that can be used to id a table (or null)
type        : <string> Table type (controlled vocabulary)
              Acceptable values:
               "OTU table"
               "Pathway table"
               "Function table"
```

```
                  "Ortholog table"
                  "Gene table"
                  "Metabolite table"
                  "Taxon table"
format-url      : <url> A string with a static URL providing format details
format-version  : <tuple> The version of the current biom format, major and minor
generated-by    : <string> Package and revision that built the table
creation-date   : <datetime> Date the table was built (ISO 8601 format)
shape           : <list of ints>, the number of rows and number of columns in data
nnz             : <int> The number of non-zero elements in the table
```

While HDF5 is a great compromise to balance the need to organize heterogeneous information in a metagenomics project and storage efficiency, its performance in terms of data loading/saving and storage/memory footprint are not as good as the formats that specifically designed for big data analytic that we are going to discuss below.

2.2.3 *Parquet and Arrow*

For decades, the vast majority of data are row-oriented storage formats, as early analysis involves reading, writing, and updating a few rows at a time. When we need to look up a single attribute from a row-oriented data format, we have to retrieve an entire row before we can decide whether or not this row is desired. If the dataset contains billions of rows, this process becomes wasteful, as the majority of the data we retrieve is discarded. Storing data in a column-oriented format, or by separately storing each attribute, skips the retrieval of irrelevant attributes and thus speeds up our query. Columnar data formats are gaining popularity as high performance access is needed for very big datasets. Apache Parquet (https://parquet.apache.org/) and Arrow (https://arrow.apache.org/) are two column-oriented file formats for data serialization (Box 1).

Box 1. **Data serialization** is the process of converting data objects present in complex data structures into a byte stream for storage, transfer, and distribution purposes on physical devices. Computer systems may vary in their hardware architecture, *OS, and memory addressing mechanisms. Source: Data Serialization - Devopedia*

To store data efficiently in the parquet format, data is serialized or converted into a series of bytes that can be stored and transferred compactly. In the de-serialization process, the data is converted back to the original structure to be analyzed. As Parquet files require decompressing and decoding before its contents can be analyzed, they achieve space/IO-efficient at the expense of CPU utilization.

While Parquet format provides advantages in archiving data on disks, its lack of rich data structure makes it not efficient for some analysis tasks such as random data lookup. Apache Arrow format also provides columnar data organization, but its structure is built for fast in-memory computing. In big data applications, the two formats are often used together, such as in Apache Spark (which we will discuss later), to store data in Parquet files and read them into memory in Arrow format.

Parquet and Arrow formats are widely used in the big data community, but their adoption in genomics and metagenomics has not been significant. Part of the reason is that the lion's share of data, metagenome sequence data is essentially lacking any structure. By now I have mentioned "data structure" several times without explanation, I will do this for our next topic: data in the context of algorithms.

2.2.4 *Data types in the context of algorithms*

In the context of algorithms, data can be classified as structured and unstructured data based on its structure (or lack thereof), or dense and sparse data based on how the information is represented. Understanding such data characteristics helps design efficient analysis algorithms.

2.2.4.1 *Structured vs unstructured data*

Structured data refers to data with a clear format or a consistent pattern (schema). The above-mentioned GFF3, TSV, and JSON formatted files are structured data. Having a well-defined blueprint or schema makes it easy to design an efficient strategy for data storage and query, since we know exactly how many bytes it takes to store our data and what type to expect for our search results. Sometimes the schema of the data can be too restrictive. In contrast, unstructured data does not have a well-defined schema, for example, image, audio, video, and metagenome sequences. For unstructured data, as they lack a predictable pattern (size, format, data type, etc), it is more difficult to design efficient storage and query methods.

Feature extraction, or mining patterns within data, is a technique that extracts useful structured information from unstructured data. As we will see in later chapters, we can assemble the unstructured metagenome read data into genomes, and then predict genes from each genome, count the frequency of each genome, etc. These processes convert unstructured data (FastQ) into structured data (TSV, GFF3, etc). This conversion process is often incomplete, however, resulting in information loss.

2.2.4.2 *Dense vs sparse data*

Suppose we want to store a large one million by one million table with the majority of its elements being zeros, we have two format choices. In a dense format, we write down each element including all zeros. In a sparse format, we could just store the nonzero elements, along with their coordinates (row and column numbers). The COOrdinate (COO) format is one of the sparse formats, as there are several others, each is suitable for a different application. Matt Eding has an excellent blog about these formats (https://matteding.github.io/2019/04/25/sparse-matrices/). It is obvious that the higher the percentage of zeros in the table (the higher sparsity), the more space we could save storing it in a sparse format. The following Table 2.5 is an example of a species abundance table represented in two formats: dense and sparse (COO).

Sparse data format is everywhere in metagenomics, for example, a species count table often has a large number of zeros due to some species being either not present or not observed in certain samples.

Table 2.5   An example of a species abundance table represented in dense and sparse formats.

Dense Format					Sparse Format		
Genome\Sample	S1	S2	S3	S4	Genome	Sample	Count
G1	0	0	3	0	G1	S3	3
G2	0	20	0	0	G2	S2	20
G3	0	0	0	17	G3	S4	17
G4	5	0	0	0	G4	S1	5

Besides saving storage space, sparse format-based computation can also perform faster and use less memory than the equivalent dense format, which is especially helpful when working with large data sets. However, for datasets that do not have sufficient sparsity (low percentage of zero values), sparse-format may not improve storage and computation efficiency, or even decrease them.

2.3 Data Governess

Here is a typical scenario at a genome sequencing center: build-in computer servers with high-throughput next-generation sequencers convert image/video data into (raw) sequence data in real-time, the sequence data is transferred to a central file storage via a high-speed network connection, the production software pipeline then analyze these data as well as the associated metadata, and these data and their associated results are finally stored into a data warehouse. Some of these data are later submitted to online data repositories, followed by being archived to long-term storage.

Whether you are a data manager for a large genome center or an individual data user, you may face the same data governess questions, although the scale might be very different. Where should the data be stored for short-term and long-term? How do I transfer a large amount of data across different locations? What type of database should I use? How do we enable data easily accessible but also ensure security and privacy?

2.3.1 *Location, location, location*

Just like a good location makes a good real estate investment, a good location is also crucial for us to store data to balance cost, security, and performance. Metagenome data are typically stored in one or more of these three types of locations: on-premises data warehouse, cloud storage, or data silos. There are also hybrid strategies to optimize performance/availability/cost, such as storing data in one place for computation while another for backup. I will explain each one and then compare these options in the context of the above data governess questions.

2.3.1.1 *On-premises data warehouse*

A on-premise, or local, data warehouse is a data management system containing both metadata and data. It is designed with high performance (fast archive and retrieve), high availability (low downtime), and scalability (growing with data volume) in mind. For sensitive data, these data warehouses also have security features to provide different levels of access to certain data. To have the ability to recover from hardware failures or disasters, a data warehouse also needs to have redundancy, such as saving another copy of the data in a different physical location. From a data user's perspective, probably the most important thing is how to easily get data out, via either an Application Programming Interface (API) or a Graphical User Interface (GUI).

Again, I will use JGI's data warehouse as an example, as it is the one I am most familiar with. The data warehouse, called JAMO (JGI Archive and Metadata Organizer), stores comprehensive information including sequence data, metadata, and analysis data. Its information can be retrieved from a web interface called JGI Genome Portal (https://genome.jgi.doe.gov/portal/, and it also provides an API (called "*jamo*") to conveniently retrieve data from the command line.

Below is the help information printed out from *jamo* that illustrates its functionality.

```
usage: jamo <command> [<args>]
jamo commands :
fetch   Retrieves files from jamo. Max number of files per call is 500
help    Prints this message
info    Prints info for the files that are returned for a query
keys    list all the keys that match your query
link    Retrieves files from jamo and links them in the current folder
report  Runs a custom report with the returned metadata
show    Shows all the metadata for a specific metadata id
```

There is a large amount of data generated by the scientific community and hosted by government-sponsored online repositories. These repositories are on a massive scale, for example, NCBI's short read archive (SRA) hosts 52.6 petabytes of sequence data as of May 2021. These hosting sites also provide toolkits and APIs for easy querying and downloading. Flexible data access models enable users to keep their private data while maintaining access to public data. Here is a short list of publicly available, nonprofit online data warehouses that contain metagenome data:

(1) NIH Short Read Archive (SRA) https://www.ncbi.nlm.nih.gov/sra
(2) EMBL-EBI MGnify https://www.ebi.ac.uk/metagenomics/
(3) DOE JGI https://img.jgi.doe.gov/

2.3.1.2 *Cloud data repository*

Many organizations that currently use on-premises data warehouses are migrating or considering to migrate their data to cloud-based data warehouses. Cloud data warehouses can provide the same functionality as the on-premises ones, minus the management hurdles. Part or the entirety of the infrastructure can be provided as a service (Infrastructure-As-A-Service, or IAAS). For example, Amazon Redshift (https://aws.amazon.com/redshift/) provides a platform for customers to deploy their data warehouses. This platform offers clusters of computer nodes with the desired amount of CPU, RAM and storage space, and it can automatically scale up or down as demand grows or shrink. Google's BigQuery (https://cloud.google.com/bigquery) takes one step further, providing both the hardware platform and the data management system. Users can interact with BigQuery as if it were an on-premises warehouse, scale up and down as needed, without knowing about the underlying computing servers altogether. For people who worry about getting locked into a particular vendor, or want to leverage multiple cloud services for extra layers of redundancy, Snowflake (https://www.snowflake.com/cloud-data-platform/) offers "data warehouse-as-a-service", and it operates across multiple cloud vendors, including Amazon Web Services (AWS) and Microsoft Azure.

Since 2020, NCBI's SRA data is available on the Google Cloud Platform (GCP) and Amazon Web Services (AWS) clouds. All publicly available, unassembled read data and authorized access human data are available for access and compute through these cloud providers. This move may signify a transition to cloud-based genomics era and other databases may follow suit.

2.3.1.3 *Data silos (such as someone's external hard drive)*

Despite the availability of data warehouses and online repositories, many researchers are still keeping their data in silos, such as their own cluster storage or external hard drives, making the data inaccessible to others. There could be a few reasons responsible for metagenomics data ended up in silos. Since small sequencing centers may not be able to afford to have on-premises data warehouses, they shift the burden of data governess to individual users. An individual user faces the choice between the cloud or their external hard drives. As the volume of metagenome data dramatically increases, so is the cost to store them on the cloud. Thus, cheap external hard drives are still the only choice for many. In many cases, they do not make backup copies of their data or safeguard them. Some researchers are unwilling to share their data, or the complicated compliance requirements imposed by online repositories prevent them from sharing. Even as government funding agencies mandate publicly funded research to be shared, various barriers still exist for the data to be accessed easily and fully.

2.3.1.4 *A comparison of storage solutions*

In summary, the data stored in silos have low cost and low performance. It does not scale and can not be accessed easily. On-premises storage can deliver very high performance, at the expense of high costs and limited scalability. Hardware system maintenance or software bugs can limit the availability of on-premises storage. In contrast, cloud storage offers high availability, and it can scale to a large scale with a reasonable performance and cost.

A comparison of the data storage reviewed in this chapter is in Table 2.6.

Table 2.6   Comparison of the data storage locations.

Features	Silos	On-premises	Cloud
Availability	Low	Medium	High
Scalability	Low	Medium	High
Performance	Low	High	Medium
Cost	Low	High	Medium
Security	Low	High	High

2.3.2 *Data ownership and usage policy*

In March 2021, DOE JGI was surprised that a preprint on BioRxiv had used its embargoed data from 15,729 JGI metagenomes, metatranscriptomes, and single cell genomes. The authors accessed this data from NCBI's SRA database where JGI's data policy on usage restriction does not apply, even though these data were automatically deposited from JGI's data warehouse. To protect the interests of its users, JGI halted all of its automated data submissions to NCBI soon after the incident.

JGI is not the only institution that places restrictions on data usage. The GISAID Initiative (https://www.gisaid.org/), which hosts data from all influenza viruses and the coronavirus causing COVID-19. It made crucial contributions to help researchers understand how viruses evolve and spread during epidemics and pandemics. GISAID also has similar data usage policies that require users to acknowledge the authors who produced its data. Distribution of data to third parties is prohibited.

Besides bringing the awareness of data usage policies to my readers, I will not go further into the controversy of these policies. The debate about data ownership and usage policy probably will continue for some time, but making data accessible to the research community broadly no doubt will promote scientific discovery.

2.4 Data Transfer

The massive volume sizes in many metagenome datasets have forced data engineers to rethink the traditional paradigms to access and process data. Making a fresh copy of a metagenome sequence data, or downloading a full copy of NCBI's microbial reference genome set, is becoming increasingly expensive in both time and cost. To efficiently process these datasets, data engineers are switching from a "bring-data-to-compute" to a "bring-compute-to-data" paradigm — instead of asking data to send to computing nodes for processing, new program models favor computing from local data sources to keep data movement at a minimum. In this section, we will discuss how we move the data around. We will explore strategies on how to process them efficiently in Chapter 4.

The best data transfer practice is actually to avoid it. Many data warehouses mentioned above support certain analysis on the spot. For example, with NCBI's toolkit (https://www.ncbi.nlm.nih.gov/toolkit), we can query the data stored there without downloading them. However, if we need to analyze the unstructured sequence data, or we need millions of queries in a short time (that exceeds the limit of API calls), we may have to download the data. Another scenario that involves moving data around is when we need to move the data from one location to another, say, from JGI-JAMO to AWS's cloud storage. Sometimes we also need to move data from a low-performance storage optimized for long-term, to a temporary but high-performance storage system to speed up data analysis.

Unless the source and target of our data transfer are in the same network, we may have to consider the impact of network speed. Many data centers have dedicated data transfer computer nodes that connect to fast networks, such as DOE's Energy Sciences Network (ESNET, https://www.es.net/) or Internet2 (http://www.internet2.edu/). Both are high-performance networks with backbones capable of transferring 100 gigabits per second (Gbps).

Another consideration for data transfer is the software tools. Traditional tools based on FTP or HTTP such as Wget, rsync, and scp are only suitable for small amounts of data. Vendor-specific tools are preferred over these tools, for example, NCBI's provides a toolkit that can download large metagenome datasets stored in the Short-Read Archive (SRA). Here, I want to highlight a tool called Globus (https://www.globus.org) , which was specifically designed for moving large research datasets between two points. It provides a secure, unified interface to your research data with its 'fire and forget' feature. As shown in Figure 2.3, with just a Globus client, a user can seamlessly move data around various data locations, as long as they have a Globus entry point.

2.5 Metagenomics Data Management: Future Perspectives and Cautions

The rate of genomics data is still growing exponentially (Figure 2.1), but the rate is slowing down. According to JGI scientist and leader of

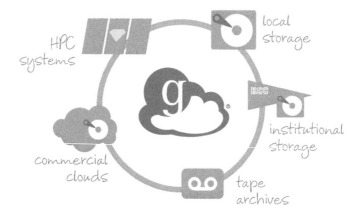

Fig. 2.3　Globus's provides a unified user interface to many data locations.
Source: https://www.globus.org/sites/all/themes/globus_bootstrap_theme/home_images/
graphic-unified@2x.png

the IMG database, Nikos Kyrpides, the growth of microbial genomes
has become linear in recent years while the exponential metagenome
sequence data growth contributes to a larger and larger proportion. It
is conceivable that metagenome sequence data growth will also become
linear, likely bounded by economical factors. In the near future, data
growth is likely driven largely by analytic pipelines that produce secondary data rather than data acquisition in web labs. We may see more
flexible JSON-based data formats that adapt to the transition from data
acquisition to data analysis. This will in turn lead to a shift from traditional relational database systems to NoSQL-based ones. This transition also brings new challenges. For example, how could we keep track
of different versions of secondary data derived from sequence data (for
example, outputs from different software tools)? How do we systematically measure the quality of these secondary data? NoSQL is great to
provide flexibility to capture outputs from different software tools, but
a poorly managed schema can actually lead to a mess.

The migration from on-premises data management systems to cloud-
based systems is currently under way. Cloud-based systems are reliable storage choices and are secure if good security practices are
implemented. However, some data governess issues still exist. As a
person's genomic sequences could be used to uniquely identify that

person, so could his/her microbiome (Franzosa *et al.*, 2015). In addition, one's microbiome data may also inevitably get "contaminated" by one's genome data. After all, human is a "super organism" consisting of our own genome and a "second genome" from our microbiome. This perspective raises the question whether or not microbiome data also need to be HIPPA compliant, and if so, what practices should be implemented to ensure the highest standards for not only security, but also privacy and ethics.

Chapter 3

Computational Metagenomics: An Algorithmic Perspective

We have discussed in the previous chapters that computational metagenomics data can be understood from three aspects: metagenomics,
data engineering, and computer algorithms — the metagenomics aspect
deals with using what information to capture to answer our science
questions; the data engineering aspect deals with how we represent and organize our data so that information can be extracted; the
algorithmic aspect deals with how data is organized so that efficient
algorithms can take advantage of. Here let us discuss the computer
algorithm aspect in computational metagenomics.

This is probably the most complex pillar of computational metagenomics, as it involves various strategies to transform the unstructured
metagenome sequence data into structured knowledge. Our algorithms
need to sort through a corpus of billions of short DNA fragments to
answer questions like what organisms in there, what they do, and how
they interact with each other. Our algorithms need to accommodate
various data formats stored in various places. More significantly, our
algorithm has to consider the large scale and the inherent noisy nature
of the data. Where do we begin this seemly infinitely daunting task?

For many computational metagenomics problems, the ability to
solve them is largely dependent on how well we are able to rephrase
them into mathematical or computational problems. For example, we
could draw an analogy between some computational metagenomics
problems with Natural Language Processing (NLP). To understand
the message in an article or a book, we perform analysis at multiple

scales: letters, words, sentence, and paragraphs. We may also learn an author's style by analyzing all of his books. Metagenome sequences can be similarly analyzed at several levels: base, kmer, gene, pathways, genome, and species. This is probably not a very good analogy to begin with, as we know, a genome is not like a text that has only a linear representation. In cells, genomic DNA is organized in complex three-dimension structures, distant parts (loci) can become physically close to each other. Nevertheless, this analogy does solve some problems, thus we will use these "scales" to organize a few algorithms as examples to explore the algorithmic pillar of computational metagenomics.

At least some of the complexity in computational metagenomics can be attributed to its multiscale nature. The five scales presented here, kmer, read, contig, genome, and metagenome, are rather from an algorithmic angle than a metagenomics one. They are chosen so that it is easier to explain the algorithms than their metagenomics counterparts: oligo, short piece, large fragment, strain, species, and community.

3.1 kmer

Genome sequences are analogous to texts consisting of four letters drawn from the alphabet A, G, C, T. Similar to the n-gram concept in the field of NLP, kmers are obtained by applying a fix-length (of k) rolling window to a given sequence. The analogy of kmers to words, however, needs to be treated carefully. First, kmers have a fixed length but words do not. More importantly, kmers do not carry biological "meaning" as words do in our language. Despite these differences, kmers can be as useful in genome analysis as words in NLP. I will try to illustrate this point in the following sections. I will not provide a comprehensive list of algorithms because there are so many of them, neither will I go into great detail explaining them. For readers in the computer science field who wish to learn more about this topic, I highly recommend an excellent book by Mäkinen *et al.*, "Genome-Scale algorithm design" (Mäkinen *et al.*, 2015).

3.1.1 *kmer frequency as sequence representation*

If you come from the genomics field, you probably are already familiar with GC-content , or the percent of G or C bases in a sequence.

GC-based analysis is a special case of kmer frequency analysis (k=1). The "Thermal Adaptation Hypothesis" (Bernardi and Bernardi, 1986) proposes that species control the GC% of their genomes as a way to adapt to their environment. For example, organisms living in hot springs tend to have high GC% so that their DNA does not melt at the high temperature in their environment. Despite its limited usage, GC-content can be very useful for some applications such as quickly identifying contaminants that are GC% outliers.

Another special case is tri- and tetra-nucleotide frequency analysis (k=3,4). Triplets within a protein-encoding gene are also called codons. Different species may have different codon usage (triplet frequency) biases. There are 256 possible tetramer combinations, and the frequency of tetra-nucleotides in prokaryotic genomes shows weak but statistically significant unique profiles.

Longer kmers enable fast sequence comparison algorithms. Here, we can rephrase the question "how similar are these two sequences" as "how similar are these two sequences if we treat them as text documents", then we can apply established algorithms for text comparison such as "Jaccard index", by transforming the two sequences into kmer frequency vectors and then comparing the two vectors. Such comparison is much faster than traditional sequence comparison methods based on sequence alignments such as BLAST. The Jaccard index can be approximated using an algorithm called minHash that reduces sequences to compressed sketch representations. Minhash is a computer algorithm originally developed to detect duplicates among large collections of documents such as email and web pages. For a detailed explanation of the algorithm, please refer to an excellent blog (http://matthewcasperson.blogspot.com/2013/11/minhash-for-dummies.html). Larger minHash sketches give a more accurate estimation of sequence similarity and are thus more sensitive to detect similarity. Smaller minHash sketches give faster speed. This algorithm is implemented in Mash (Ondov *et al.*, 2016), which did an all-vs-all comparison between 54,118 genomes in 150 cpu hours with a sensitive setting.

Longer kmers can also be used for taxonomy classification. By cataloging species-specific kmers, or sets of kmers only occur in a specific species, we can infer the presence of this species when its unique kmers are observed. Kraken is one of the algorithms that are based on this principle, and it can classify over 1 million reads per minute on a single machine (Wood and Salzberg, 2014).

In many algorithms based on kmers, its size, k, must be carefully considered. As there are 4^k all possible kmers, a larger k yields a higher dimensional, more sparse representation of a sequence. A larger kmer captures more information of the sequence. A smaller k, on the other hand, yields a lower dimensional and more dense representation, but it loses more information because transforming a sequence into kmers is a lossy operation. In the machine learning context, kmers are often treated as "features" of the sequence. Recent advances in deep learning also prompt researchers to explore kmer embedding methods to facilitate species identification (Woloszynek *et al.*, 2019). It is worth noting that although I only mentioned nucleotide kmers here, protein kmers are also very useful to design algorithms to predict protein function.

Using large kmers on large sequence datasets can easily generate a large number of kmers, which requires a large amount of RAM or disk space, as well as significantly slows the kmer based matching algorithms. To achieve the space efficiency of these algorithms, Roberts *et al.* developed the concept of "minimizers" as a reduced representation of kmers (Roberts *et al.*, 2004). A (w, k)-minimizer of a sequence is the smallest kmer (of a chosen order, e.g. lexicographical) in a surrounding window of w consecutive kmers on both strands. Therefore, a minimizer can represent $2w$ kmers, which dramatically reduces storage and speeds up kmer matching computations by a large factor, with only slightly reduced sensitivity.

We only discussed perfect kmers in the above. What if there are errors in the sequence, as we discussed in Chapter 1, caused by imperfect sequencing technologies? Well, there are at least two solutions. First, we could filter out the sequence errors and potentially correct them by performing kmer analysis. Figure 3.1 illustrates the kmer frequency from an ideal NGS dataset. Error-containing kmers can be filtered out using a threshold that favors removing errors. Second, we could apply algorithms that tolerate errors, such as locality-sensitive hashes.

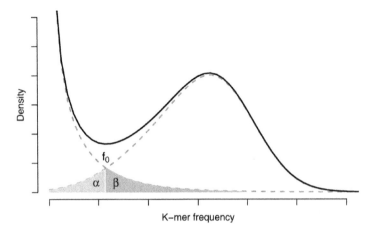

K–mer frequency

Fig. 3.1 Kmer frequency and sequence errors. A kmer frequency histogram (black solid line) is a formed by both error-free (blue dashed) and error-containing k-mers (orange dashed) for a NGS data set. An empirical threshold ($f0$) is used to filter out error-containing kmers, resulting the loss of some error-free kmers (α-labeled area) and the remaining error-containing kmers (β-labeled area). The peak corresponds to the sequencing coverage of the genome. kmer frequency histograms from real metagenomic datasets often do not show clear peaks due to the presence of many genomes. Credit: Image is from (Zhao *et al.*, 2018). Reproduced with CC-BY 4.0 licence.

Decomposing a sequence into kmers transforms the unstructured sequence into structured kmer frequency tables or kmer to sequence maps. During this transformation, we lose some sequence information, such as the order of the kmers in the sequence. Despite this, the kmer frequency table (also called sequence composition) is a numerical structured format, which enables fast, approximate algorithms such as the sequence-sequence comparison and species identification methods discussed in this chapter.

3.1.2 *kmer graph as sequence representation*

We can add order information to link the above kmers and create a new data structure: directed graphs. Intuitively, we can use kmers as nodes of the graph and use their overlaps as edges. As adjacent kmers overlap by $k-1$ bases, the edges between connected nodes are also $k-1$ bases. If all kmers from this sequence appear only once, then the graph becomes a linked list. This is seldom the case, however. kmers

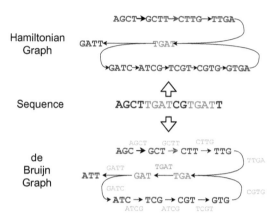

Fig. 3.2   A Hamiltonian and a de Bruijn graph from the same sequence.

often occur multiple times in the sequence, which create loops. This type of graph is called Hamiltonian graph. Alternatively, we could use the overlap between kmers as nodes and kmers as edges to create a de Bruijn graph. Using a simple sequence, we can create two kmer graphs shown in Figure 3.2.

Representing sequences as graphs opens the door to established graph algorithms. Do we lose information by transforming sequences into graphs? In the above example, the answer is no. As we can walk either graph (graph traversal) to recover the original sequence. In the Hamiltonian graph, we start from the beginning node (kmer) and visit each node exact once until we stop at the last node. In the de Bruijn graph, we try to visit each edge exact once instead.

An interesting characteristic of the kmer graph is that we will get the same graph whether we start from a genome, or the reads obtained from this genome (as long as the reads cover the entire genome). The de Bruijn graph is the basic data structure for many metagenome assembly algorithms, a topic we will cover in Chapter 8. Why not the Hamiltonian graph? It turned out traversing a large Hamiltonian graph is NP-complete (computer science jargon to describe a hard problem). More explanations can be found in a nice article (Compeau *et al.*, 2011).

About the de Bruijn graph and its traversal, there is actually a great story about the great mathematician Leonhard Euler. Three hundred years ago, in the Prussian city of Königsberg (present day Kaliningrad

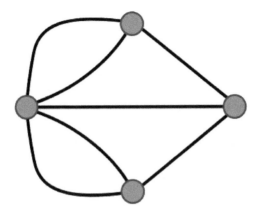

Fig. 3.3   The seven bridge problem.
Source: Wikimedia Common https://commons.wikimedia.org/wiki/File: K%C3%
B6nigsberg_graph.svg.

in Russia), seven bridges (edges) joined the four parts of the city (nodes)
shown as Figure 3.3. At that time people were wondering, is it possible to visit every part of the city by walking across each of the seven
bridges exactly once and returning to one's starting location? Attempts
kept failing until in 1735 Euler brought the Eulerian path concept
and proved that such a problem is only solvable if a Eulerian path
exists. This is not the case for the seven bridges problem, unfortunately. Euler's theory later became the first theorem of modern graph
theory.

kmer is widely used in computational metagenomics, and it is the
foundation of many computing algorithms. We only briefly discussed a
few examples. In later chapters, we will meet them over and over.

3.2 Read

From an algorithm perspective, this basic unit that comes off a
sequencer is versatile. They can be represented as sets of kmers and
used to identify microbial species in the reference database with tools
such as Kraken (Wood and Salzberg, 2014). They can be used to construct a de Bruijn graph from which genomes can be assembled, as they
contain kmer connectivity information. From a metagenomics perspective, each read is an independent observation of a species, therefore

from the reads one could infer the abundance statistics of many species in a community, and track their changes over time.

If the species we are interested among the microbial community has a reference genome, then we can accurately quantify the species by mapping the reads to its reference genome. This process, short read alignment, is one of the basic tasks in model organism genomics. In the metagenomics setting, read mapping needs a detour as reference genomes are not available and one has to assemble the reads to obtain the reference.

The read alignment problem in computational metagenomics is the following: we start with millions to billions of reads and one or more large reference sequences (assembled contigs or genomes), and we want to find what reads match what reference sequence and optionally report all matching positions. A straight-forward solution is to construct a dictionary with every possible kmers (with k equals to the length of the read) of the reference and their locations. We can then use this dictionary to locate each read as a kmer in a reference. However, this solution is neither space- or time-efficient: the dictionary will be large for large reference genome(s); and for a different set of reads with different lengths, we would have to rebuild the lookup dictionary.

From a computer algorithm view point, the alignment problem is equivalent to locating shorter substrings among large strings. This view inspires us to look for existing algorithms that can efficiently find substrings of a string. We are in luck again, as the Burrow-Wheeler transformation (BWT) and FM-index (Burrows and Wheeler, 1994; Ferragina and Manzini, 2000) elegantly solved this problem. The idea is to transform the reference genome using BWT so it can be easily compressed and stored, and all of its sub-strings can be quickly found. The time needed to map a short read only depends on the length of the short read, not the length of the reference sequence. This algorithm led to breakthroughs in short read alignment and inspired tools such as BWA (Li and Durbin, 2009) and Bowtie2 (Langmead and Salzberg, 2012).

For long noisy reads such as those from PacBio or ONT sequencing technologies, BWT-based alignment algorithms will fail. Even if we can correct the sequence errors in long reads (a topic to discuss in Chapter 5), BWT-based algorithms will become slow as read length increases. Given the error distribution within a long read is nonrandom, we can expect that there are "stretches" of perfect segments in a long read. Algorithms such as Minimap maps a long read to a reference based on a linear chain of matched minimizers between the two (Li, 2016). The second version, Minimap2, has become a versatile mapper and pairwise aligner for nucleotide sequences including both DNA and spliced mRNA. It works with both short reads, long reads, and even full-length genomes (Li, 2018). Modeling the comparison between two sequences as matching patterns of minimizers makes Minimap a generic sequence comparison tool.

3.3 Contig

A contig refers to the contiguous DNA sequence constructed from a set of overlapping short reads through the genome assembly process, representing the sequence of a genome or a genomic region. We will discuss the metagenome assembly process in Chapter 8. Depending on the quality of the assembly process, the length of contigs can vary greatly, from a few hundreds of bases to hundreds of kilobases. Most of them are still much shorter than genomes, but they can be much longer than reads, thus supporting a more robust analysis than kmers and reads in applications such as species identification. The above read-based analysis is also called "primary analysis". In "secondary analysis", we solve problems like predicting genes from assembled contigs, classifying taxonomy, discovering new enzymes or pathways, etc.

Just like a sentence, a gene also has structure. For prokaryotic protein coding genes, they have an open reading frame (ORF, with start and stop codons), a ribosomal binding site (RBS) to initiate translation. If they are organized in an operon, they also share a promoter and a terminator for transcription. Because genes are more conserved than noncoding regions, their sequence compositions also show distinct characteristics, such as higher GC-content. Combining these structural characteristics, Hyatt *et al.* developed a gene prediction algorithm called Prodigal (PROkaryotic DYnamic programming Gene-finding ALgorithm) (Hyatt *et al.*, 2010). Identifying eukaryotic protein-coding genes, however, is inherently more challenging due to the exon-intron architecture of an eukaryotic gene. Current methods heavily rely on the availability of transcriptomics data.

Prodigal predicts genes using an expert model with manually selected features combined with simple rules we learned over time. If a gene has a homolog in the reference database, then we can also infer its function or classification based on its known homologs. For example, for taxonomy classification, we would search the small subunit of ribosomal RNA genes in our metagenome dataset on online repositories such as the SILVA database (https://www.arb-silva.de/). Homology search in the context of metagenomics carries a computational burden, however. SILVA already contains over 9 million small subunit (ssu rRNA) entries in its version SSU 138.1. It would take QIIME, the most popular software tool for taxonomy classification based on SSU rRNA, more than 58 hours to index the SILVA database and days to search a large dataset (Lu and Salzberg, 2020). Running the golden standard tool for homology search, Blast, to search millions of gene candidates against billions of reference genes, is computationally expensive. The above mentioned Kraken has been used for faster SSU rRNA classification (Lu and Salzberg, 2020). For generic protein homology search, DIAMOND (double index alignment of next-generation sequencing data) achieves 4 orders of magnitude of speedup over Blast by leveraging several algorithms, including reduced sequence representation, spaced seeds, and indexing both the query and reference for fast comparison (Buchfink *et al.*, 2015).

Discovering genes encoding novel enzymes from long assembled contigs or long reads from bacteria and fungi brings bioprospecting to the next level. To discover novel bioactive compounds with potential pharmaceutical applications such as antibiotics, now it is even possible to rapidly and reliably predict an entire biosynthetic gene cluster for a compound. This is a very challenging problem, several algorithms (gene cluster prediction, reference cluster homology search, domain homology search, and chemical structure prediction) were stacked together for this complex task (Medema *et al.*, 2011).

We will revisit gene structure and function prediction in detail in Chapter 7.

3.4 Genome

Having the high-quality genome assembly makes some of the analyses based on kmers, reads, and contigs more robust. For example, compared with SSU rRNA-based taxonomy classification, genome-based methods not only produce more coherent results by resolving conflicts (Hugenholtz *et al.*, 2016), they can also classify genomes without SSUs such as virus and phages. With a genome containing a full set of genes, we can infer all metabolic pathways in this organism using the MetaCyc Metabolic Pathway Database (https://metacyc.org/) and unveil its metabolic capacity or potential.

As the whole is greater than the sum of its parts, a genome sequence opens the door to many possibilities. For example, Zymomonas mobilis ZM4 is a bacterium that can efficiently produce ethanol from various carbon substrates and can tolerate up to 16% ethanol. Lee et al. combined automated genome annotation, literature search and manual revision to build a genome-scale metabolic model of this 2 Mb genome, composed of 601 reactions and 579 metabolites (Figure 3.4) (Lee *et al.*, 2010). To make this network "functional", or to simulate the bacterium's metabolism, traditional methods rely on computationally

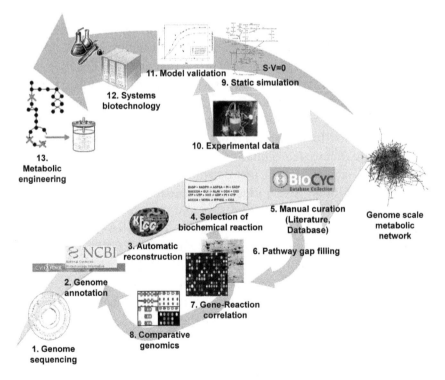

Fig. 3.4   Procedure for the reconstruction of genome-scale metabolic network in Z. mobilis and its application to metabolic engineering. Reproduced from (Lee *et al.*, 2010) with CC-BY 2.0 licence.

intensive differential equations. In contrast, Flux Balance Analysis (FBS) represents the metabolic network as a set of linear equations and solves it by linear programming. By making assumptions that the network is in a steady state and optimized for biomass growth, it requires very little information in terms of the enzyme kinetic parameters and concentration of metabolites in the cell. As a result, FBS takes only seconds on a personal computer to solve.

3.5 Metagenome

Producing a catalog of microbial species only solved the composition problem, i.e., who is there in the community. We are more interested to know how these species, together, define an ecological function and how they respond to environmental changes. By tracing the same microbial community over time in a time-series study, or by comparing multiple communities, we may learn metagenome-scale insights.

Before whole-genome sequencing dominants metagenomics, ecologists heavily relied on the composition of a community based on SSU-based taxonomy profiling as a proxy for its function. For example, more diversity in a gut microbiome suggests a healthier individual. However, diversity measure is often a poor predictor for ecological function. To improve this, Ramírez-Flandes *et al.* used 247 microbial metagenomes from 18 biomes to determine whether each set of genes performs better in characterizing global ecological differences (Figure 3.5(a)). They found oxidoreductase genes can effectively differentiate these biomes, while other categories of enzymes, general protein-coding genes, transporter genes, and taxonomic gene markers can not (Figure 3.5(b)). Functional diversity, instead of taxonomic diversity, is relevant for understanding biomes and quantifying the impact of environmental stressors on them (Ramírez-Flandes *et al.*, 2019).

In the above study, the correlations between sets of genes and ecological functions were calculated using their pairwise maximal information coefficients (MIC). As part of the maximal information-based nonparametric exploration (MINE) statistics, MIC uncovers variables that not only have functional associations but are also statistically independent. The combinatorial nature of MIC calculation with thousands

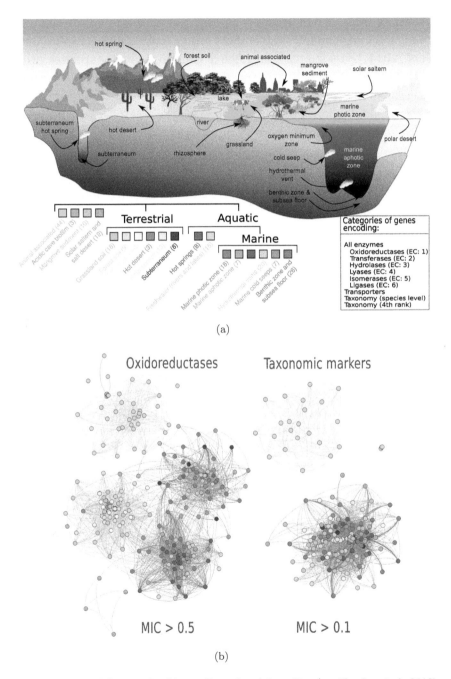

(a)

(b)

Fig. 3.5 An earth biome-microbiome. Reproduced from (Ramírez-Flandes *et al.*, 2019) with CC-BY 2.0 licence.

of sets of genes could take a long time. As each pair of MIC can be computed independently, the authors used a tool called RapidMic (Tang *et al.*, 2014) by taking the advantage of modern computer architectures' hardware-level parallelism to speed up calculation. We will cover more topics about hardware and software parallelism in the next chapter.

3.6 Conclusion and Future Perspectives

The success of many metagenomics problems largely depends on whether or not we can formulate them as a computer science or mathematics problem. Simpler tasks have taken advantage of available computer algorithms. Complex tasks are convoluted, with no obvious similar problems in computer science. Strategies to solve complex problems tend to break them into simpler problems via a "divide-and-conquer" approach. For problems without sound solutions, a common strategy is to take an "ensemble algorithm": combining multiple available algorithms to yield better results.

Although it has been long postulated that it is possible to apply the language models we learned from NLP to solve genomics problems, they have not been widely adopted in practice. It should be possible to learn the structure of the genome to identify genes while learning their semantics (gene function), at least for simple genomes such as viruses. Recently, this is accomplished by applying NLP to construct models that predict how mutations affect fitness and escape from the host immune system. By using a word-embedding algorithm, the authors were able to build models for influenza A hemagglutinin, HIV-1 envelope glycoprotein, and severe acute respiratory syndrome coronavirus 2 (SARS-CoV-2) spike glycoprotein (Hie *et al.*, 2021).

The fast pace of advancement in computational metagenomics drives the availability of bigger databases and datasets. With the influx of metagenomics data, manual steps will gradually be displaced by data-driven, automated algorithms. On 30 September 2012, the deep learning-based AlexNet beat previous expert-based image classification systems by a large margin, achieving an error rate more than 10.8 percentage points lower than that of the runner-up (Krizhevsky *et al.*, 2012). AlexNet does the trick by training on 1.2 million images without expert input about the rules of image classification. In 2016, a team lead by Craig Venter sequenced 10,000 human genomes. After they stacked these genome together and visualized the regions devoid of variations, the structure of genes becomes apparent without any prior knowledge (Telenti *et al.*, 2016). I could imagine that in the future many challenging metagenomics problems may be solved not by smart algorithms, but by large amount of dumb data.

Chapter 4

Hardware and Software Aspects for Scalable Analysis

Let us go back to the analogy we made at the beginning of the book. We relate a computational metagenomics problem to a transportation problem. By now, we should have some knowledge of the terrain: metagenomics problems and data types. We have mapped out our routes: computer algorithms that help us process metagenome data. Now it is time to deal with the vehicles that will take us to our destination faster: hardware and software for computational metagenomics. In this chapter, we will discuss the various hardware and software choices available to us, and how to make the right choice so that we will efficiently process the specific data.

The metagenome data problem is also a big data problem, and it shares these four basic characteristics:

(1) Volume. Depending on number of species in a community, we need to produce a large volume of data. In a typical experiment we have tens of Gigabases of data, a human microbiome project produced 500 Gb, our cow rumen project produced 1.2 Tb, and the biggest project to date, a world-wide ocean survey project produced 8 Tb. Based on what we have learned about these projects, to get a fair coverage of the microbes in soil, we would need sequence at least 200 Tb.

(2) Variety. Besides metagenomic data, a multi-omics project can also produce metatranscriptomic, metaproteomic, and metabolic data. There are different types of metadata as well, such as image,

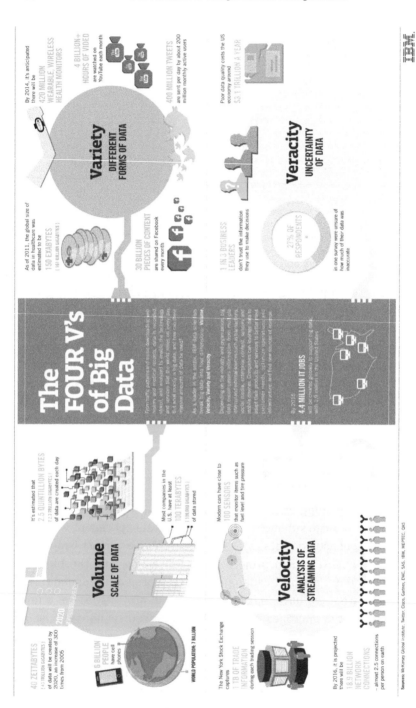

Fig. 4.1   The four V's of Big Data.

audio and textual data. We covered some of these types of data in Chapter 2.

(3) Velocity. Modern sequencers and sensors deployed in the field are generating data in an unprecedented speed. Innovations in genome technologies keep generating new data varieties and larger volumes, posing more challenges in velocity.

(4) Veracity. We have learned that different sequencing technologies have different error rates in Chapter 1. Metagenome data can be contaminated during data-generation process, including biological contaminants such as host data, technological contaminants such as sequencing adapters. If amplification is used, uneven coverage biases could be introduced. Missing data is also a common problem in metagenomics data. I will devote a whole chapter to discuss data quality issues and how to improve them in Chapter 5.

Genomics big data is not typical big data. Besides the above four Vs, genomics big data also has a "U", which means the majority of genomics data are unstructured. Unstructured data is inherently much harder than structured data to analyze. The "U" makes the four Vs worse. We often need 200 times of space for temporary data, and we use a variety of software tools that generate more varieties of data, and these tools inevitably introduce additional noise and biases on top of those coming from the original data.

The above challenges in big metagenomics data also make it exciting. In the past 10 years, while I am working on this problem, through many failures, I gradually realize the ideal solution should have four criteria: easy to implement, robustness, scale with data, and efficient. I put easy to implement on the top of my list. The metagenomics field does not have access to many experienced software engineers, many data analysts that come from biological sciences prefer scripting programming languages over engineer-level languages. The rapid change of technologies constantly changes our data, existing software tools need to rapidly adapt to these changes to avoid being obsoleted. As other big data solutions, the ideal computational metagenomics solutions should be robust, able to scale to data, and efficient.

It is not possible to cover this broad topic in just one chapter. I will discuss a few common choices we face in computational metagenomics in an "A vs B" format. In many cases, the choice depends on the underlying data and problem, as well as our budget for the project. The general rule of thumb is that we should seek a choice that is scalable to big data, robust to failures, easy to implement, and low cost. Below we will discuss various choices to achieve scalable analyses, in the context of these four aspects.

4.1 Hardware Scaling

When I started to work on the cow rumen metagenomics project back in 2009, our first batch of Illumina short reads was totalled at 17 giga bases (Gb). By today's standards this amount is tiny, but at that time this was our biggest dataset and we could not find a single computer that has big enough memory to assemble it using velvet, the one and only available short-read assembler at that time. I took this need-for-memory problem to a hardware engineer at JGI, Jeremy Brand, who later worked out a computer system to help our project as illustrated in Figure 4.2.

From a hardware system architect's perspective, my request for a system with the biggest memory available can not be simply solved by

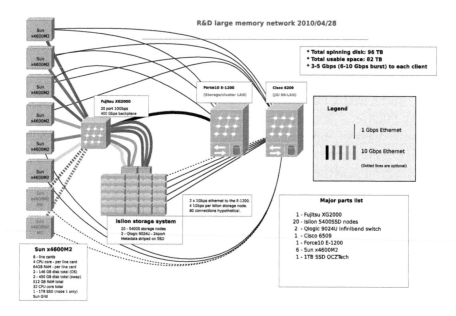

Fig. 4.2   A large memory system designed in 04/2010 for metagenomics.

plugging in more memory modules on a machine. If the file storage system (local hard drives, network file system) is not fast enough, the machine would just spend most of its time waiting for data to be loaded. While the size of the physical memory (RAM) determines the largest data that could be processed, it is often the speed of the file system, or the performance of input/output (IO), measured in IOPS (input/output operations per second), that becomes a bottleneck. Jeremy's solution for file system IO was a three-pronged strategy: (1) using local solid state drives (SSDs) for caching intermediate files during analysis, as SSDs are much faster than traditional magnetic hard drives; (2) using multiple SSDs in parallel to further improve IO performance; and (3) using faster network connections between computing nodes and the network file system (10 gigabits links, fastest at that time).

While building this large system, we applied both vertical and horizontal scaling techniques commonly used in the high-performance (HPC) computing community. The distinction of these two scaling methods is illustrated in Figure 4.3. In vertical scaling, we increased the capacity in a single machine: 512GB RAM, 32 CPUs from the largest server at that time (128 GB and 16 CPUs). We also increased the number of machines from 1 to 6 in horizontal scaling.

Vertical scaling

As the research community wanted bigger memory to assembly large plant genomes and metagenomes, vertical scaling was the preferred choice because the assemblers at that time can only work on a

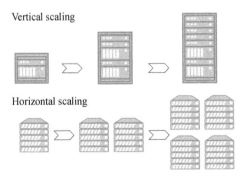

Fig. 4.3 Vertical vs Horizontal scaling.

single machine. These machines with large memory enabled large metagenome assembly projects, without the extensive time or effort required to reengineer the software tools for multiple nodes. However, vertical scaling comes with a steep cost, each of the nodes in our big memory system cost $50,000. And it is much harder to add more memory. In July 2010, the Pittsburgh Supercomputing Center (PSC) built a shared-memory system, Blacklight, which has 4,096 CPU cores and 32 terabytes (TB) of memory, a system costing $2.8 million. Despite this, these systems can still be the preferred choice in exploratory studies when the time to get results outweighs the computing cost. With the availability of large memory nodes via cloud computing, people only need to pay a small cost to use these nodes rather than to build them. For example, AWS offers several instances with 9, 12, 18, and 24 TB of instance memory in 2019 (https://aws.amazon.com/blogs/aws/ec2-high-memory-update-new-18-tb-and-24-tb-instances/). The 12TB instance, u-12tb1, costs up to $67 per hour to use.

Besides adding more memory, more storage, and more CPUs to a single machine, vertical scaling also includes adding co-processors, such as field-programmable gate arrays (FPGA)(Wikipedia, 2019a), graphics-processing units (GPU)(Wikipedia, 2019b), and tensor processing unit (TPU)(Jouppi *et al.*, 2017). These special hardware architectures could be extremely helpful for a subset of metagenomics tasks that are computing-intensive. However, unlike the above big memory machines, these architectures require reengineering existing software tools before one can take advantage of them.

Horizontal scaling

Scaling up by upgrading the existing nodes with more capacity (cores, memory, co-processing unit, storage, etc) as we discussed above can be very costly beyond a certain point. Alternatively, we can do horizontal scaling, or scale out, by adding more computing nodes to form a computing cluster. The practice that aggregates the computing power of many computers to deliver much higher performance than a single computer is called high-performance computing (HPC). The above HPC system we built at JGI is a small-scale system with 6 computers or nodes. Many modern HPC systems contain hundreds of nodes. Measured by floating-point operations per second (flops), these systems can deliver petaflops (1e12) computing performance instead of teraflops (1e9) of that of a typical desktop computer or workstation. Some of the world's top HPC systems take horizontal scaling to an extreme scale to make supercomputers. For example, the TOP500 list that publishes the world's fastest supercomputers, saw the top spot, the Japanese Fugaku supercomputer, to set a new world record to have 7,630,848 cores 442 petaflops in November 2020 (https://www.top500. org/lists/top500/2020/11/).

While delivering shocking computing performance, HPC has many disadvantages. They are always on whether or not being used, incurring high costs for power consumption. These systems require a professional team for maintenance and upgrading, and each maintenance likely makes the system unavailable for a period of time. These systems are often located in one centralized location, which makes them vulnerable to unpredictable events such as power shutoffs. In addition, in order to achieve a high utilization rate, the systems are shared by many users. These systems are not able to isolate different types of workloads, as one rogue user may overwhelm the entire system. Extensive training is often required before one can start to use these systems.

4.1.1 *Managed or hosted hardware scaling on the cloud*

By now, you probably have realized that managing hardware is a cumbersome task and it does not contribute to the productivity of a computational metagenomics researcher. Wouldn't it be nice if someone else does this for us, so our data analysis tasks always get sufficient computing resources whenever we need them and as however big we need them?

The answer is definitely yes. Thanks to virtualization and cloud computing technologies, both vertical and horizontal hardware scaling can be easily done with only a few mouse clicks and without expensive hardware procurement or hiring experienced hardware engineers. In recent years, cloud computing has evolved to address the above limitations we discussed in hardware scaling. There are quite a few cloud computing vendors, such as Amazon Web Services (AWS), Google Cloud Platform (GCP), Microsoft Azure Cloud, etc. We will use AWS as an example to explain several key concepts of cloud computing and learn the opportunity it provides to significantly reduce the time and cost associated with scalable data analysis.

4.1.1.1 *Amazon Machine Image (AMI)*

Stands for Amazon Machine Image. It is a template of a software environment (operating system or OS, libraries, software configuration, personal data, etc), from which one can launch one or more instances. An instance is analogous to a workstation, although it is virtual. One AMI can be instantiated into many instances, each with a different hardware setup (CPU, RAM, storage, etc). We can create an AMI from a running instance, make changes to the instance (install or update software, adding/removing data), and then create a new AMI for later use. With the same AMI, we can then launch a fleet of instances to achieve horizontal scaling with just a few clicks!

We can also share our AMI with the community and use an AMI from the community, often to reduce the time needed to set up our software environment. We could use commercial AMIs from the "AWS Marketplace", and some may incur additional costs on top of AWS's.

Conceptually, AMI is similar to docker containers. The difference lies in that a docker container is more lightweight and portable. A docker container often contains a very small set of software and can be ported to various platforms, while an AMI contains an entire machine (except for the hardware) and is locked to the AWS ecosystem.

4.1.1.2 *Amazon Elastic Compute Cloud (EC2)*

An EC2 instance is a virtual machine initiated from an AMI. It can be stopped(paused), resumed, and terminated. Launching an instance needs an AMI, a machine type (CPU/RAM), a network, and a storage system.

A running EC2 instance incurs charges depending on the resources it consumes. To reduce its cost, we need to carefully choose the machine types to maximize resource utilization. For example, the short-read mapping tasks such as BWA benefit from a server with many CPU cores but not necessarily a large amount of RAM, therefore, we could choose a compute-optimized instance such as a c5.9xlarge machine with 36 cores. In contrast, short-read assemblers like MetaSpades often require large amounts of RAM, therefore we could choose a memory-optimized type such as r5.8xlarge with 32 cores and 256 GB RAM. More information about EC2 instance types is available at https://aws.amazon.com/ec2/instance-types/.

We can change the machine type of an instance after it is stopped. Here is a useful trick to save money for a large computing job: we can begin with a small instance, install the software tools and libraries necessary for the job, get the data ready, test the setup to make sure it works, and then stop it and switch to a larger instance type, without the need to repeat the software configuration, to run the large job. This is how easy "virtual" vertical scaling gets!

AWS also offers reserved and spot instances, which can further reduce the costs in an volume-/auction-based pricing model comparing the normal mode (on-demand). Spot instances can offer large discounts when using a large instance type or many instances. For a large job, we can combine the previous trick and spot instance to get more cost-saving. After we set up the software environment for a large job in the previous step, we can save it as a new AMI image. We then launch a large spot instance from it and run the large job. One downside is that the spot instance system is based on a bidding system, it can be outbid by higher priority bidders, and your workload will be disrupted if that happens. There are a few ways to minimize this kind of disruption including setting a high bidding price, taking snapshots, etc.

4.1.1.3 *Elastic Block Storage (EBS), Elastic File System (Amazon EFS) and Simple Storage System (S3)*

Amazon EFS, Amazon EBS, and Amazon S3 are AWS' three different storage types for different types of workload needs.

Amazon Elastic Block Storage (EBS) delivers high-availability block-level storage volumes for EC2 instances. It stores data on a file system that is retained after the EC2 instance is shut down. It stores data in equally sized blocks and organizes them into a hierarchy similar to a traditional file system. The size and performance of an EBS volume can be manually configured based on your workload needed in a way similar to a local disk drive on a physical machine.

Amazon Elastic File System (EFS) offers scalable file storage, also optimized for EC2. It scales up and down automatically to meet dynamic workloads. EFS can be mounted on different AWS services and accessed from all your virtual machines. EFS is equivalent to network file systems (NFS).

The main difference between EBS and EFS is that EBS is only accessible from a single EC2 instance in your particular AWS region, while EFS allows you to mount the file system across multiple regions and instances.

Amazon Simple Storage System (S3) is an object store good at storing vast numbers of backups or user files. Unlike EBS or EFS, S3 is not limited to EC2. Files stored within an S3 bucket can be accessed programmatically or directly from services such as AWS CloudFront. Each object has its own unique identifier or key, for access through web requests from any location. S3 also supports static web content hosting that can be accessed from the S3 bucket or from AWS CloudFront. And S3 is notably secure by providing "eleven nines" - 99.999999999% of annual data durability. That means one would likely be able to keep one billion objects without losing a single one for a hundred years.

4.1.1.4 Virtual Private Cloud (VPC)

Amazon Virtual Private Cloud (Amazon VPC) is AWS's virtual network service that closely resembles a traditional network but with the benefits of using the scalable infrastructure of AWS. A virtual private cloud (VPC) is a virtual network dedicated to your AWS account. We can launch our EC2 instances into a logically isolated network with a VPC to ensure security.

Almost all cloud computing vendors offer similar core components of infrastructure: hardware configuration, OS templates, scalable storage, and virtual networks.

4.2 Software Scaling

As hardware, software tools also need to scale to data. In parallel computing, or carrying out multiple operations simultaneously, software can take advantage of the underlying hardware using one of the two strategies: task parallelism or data parallelism.

4.2.1 *Task parallelism*

In task parallelism, our big computational metagenomics problem is modeled as a big task, which is further divided into many small tasks. Each task can then be executed on a thread. Many threads, either on the same multiple processor machine or on multiple machines, are executed in parallel to fully utilize the available processors and memory. One example of task parallelism would be the short-read alignment problem. Short-read aligners would create multiple tasks, with each task working on a chunk of data. Through a task scheduler, each task is then assigned to a separate thread for parallel processing.

Several programming models are currently available for task parallelism. We will discuss a few common choices here.

4.2.1.1 *Open MP*

OpenMP is the a programming interface primarily used for shared memory systems. In this programming model, all threads or processes have access to all data in the shared memory. Programmers have more control over each thread's behavior in OpenMP. Driven by the popularity of shared-memory multiple-core systems, there are many OpenMP-based tools such as SPAdes(Bankevich *et al.*, 2012).

4.2.1.2 *Message Passing Interface (MPI)*

OpenMP is limited to a single machine with shared memory. For HPC systems with distributed memory (see above for horizontal scaling 4.3), the Message Passing Interface (MPI) is a standard choice for task parallelism. MPI is a programming interface that specifies how tasks are synchronized and how data are exchanged through messages across nodes within a HPC cluster. MPI allows programmers to specify what content is exchanged (Wikipedia, 2019c). MPI-based NGS short-read aligner pBWA(Peters *et al.*, 2012) and assembler such as Ray(Boisvert *et al.*, 2012), which can scale up to hundreds of thousands cores on a HPC cluster.

Besides OpenMP and MPI, there are other task-parallel programming models. One example is PGAS(Wikipedia, 2019d), is a distributed shared-memory programming model that combines the advantages of OpenMP and MPI. Unified Parallel C (UPC, 2002) and UPC++(Zheng *et al.*, 2014) are C and C++ extensions of PGAS model, respectively. UPC-based tools like Meta-HipMer(Georganas *et al.*, 2018) can assemble a 2.6 Tb metagenome dataset in just 3.5 hours on 512 nodes.

The biggest drawback of programming models based on task parallelism is that they are in general hard to program. Experienced software engineers are required to handle issues such as memory locality, data communication, and task synchronization. Software tools may take a significant time to develop, combined with the rapid changes in metagenomics data, inevitably drive up the development and maintenance costs. Some recent community efforts aim to combine the ease of programming such as Python with the superior efficiency of task parallelism, e.g., the RAY project (https://github.com/ray-project/ray) and DASK (https://dask.org/), which may encourage more metagenomics applications to take full advantage of modern HPC systems.

4.2.2 *Data parallelism*

When the volume of the data being processed is getting big, moving it around to where computing happens within the HPC system is getting more expensive. If we could do computing locally, we would save time by avoiding moving data too frequently. In data parallelism, the data itself is divided and distributed across multiple CPUs or computing nodes, where the same operations are performed on each subset in parallel. One example of data parallelism would be to divide the input data into subsets and pass it to the threads performing the same task on different CPUs. Hadoop and Spark are two examples of data parallelism.

4.2.2.1 *Apache Hadoop*

The Apache Hadoop has two core components: a Hadoop Distributed File System (HDFS), and an MapReduce programming model. A big file is stored in small chunks that spread across a Hadoop cluster. These chunks are replicated (default 3 times) and different copies are located on different nodes, which ensures the data will not be lost in the event of the failure of a node. To process these small chunks, the node manager sends out "mapper" jobs and nodes run these jobs on their local data before sending back the result. The results are then combined via "reducer" jobs, into the final result.

Compared with OpenMP and MPI, Hadoop offers advantages including data redundancy and data locality. In addition, communication between nodes is much lighter in Hadoop than MPI. However, Hadoop relies on disk storage to store its computing objects, and its IO-intensive nature makes Hadoop-based solutions inefficient compared to its equivalent implementations in MPI and OpenMP. Since there is no state shared between individual mapper and reducer tasks, Hadoop is not suitable for iterative tasks, which limits its application to only a small number of metagenomcis problems. Several Hadoop-based applications have been developed for genomics, to name a few, NGS read alignment (Zou *et al.*, 2015; Abuín *et al.*, 2015), genetic variant calling (Hung *et al.*, 2011), sequence analysis(Nordberg *et al.*, 2013; Shi *et al.*, 2017).

4.2.2.2 *Apache Spark*

To overcome the limitations of Hadoop, Apache Spark, which started as a research project at the UC Berkeley AMPLab in 2009, innovated in a few aspects over Hadoop. First of all, Spark relies primarily on in-memory computing. It caches most of its computing objects in memory, which has much better IO performance than those on disk. Second, Spark optimizes MapReduce task execution via a DAG (Directed Acyclic Graph) scheduler. Third, Spark supports iterative options, which opens the door to many new applications that require iteration. Finally, Spark greatly improves programmability: it allows users to write applications quickly in Scala, Java, Python, R, and SQL; it includes libraries for Spark SQL (DataFrames and Datasets), MLlib (Machine Learning), GraphX (Graph Processing), and DStreams (Spark Streaming); one can run Spark using a variety of cluster managers: its standalone cluster manager, Apache Hadoop YARN, Mesos, or Kubernetes.

Many Spark-based genomics applications have been developed for large-scale sequence processing on public or private cloud systems (Guo *et al.*, 2018; Shi *et al.*, 2018; Zhou *et al.*, 2017) and for a comprehensive review please refer to (Guo *et al.*, 2018).

Despite its early success, there are several challenges faced by the data parallelism programming model. Although in-memory data processing has significantly improved IO performance, it still can be an order of magnitude slower than MPI-based implementations. Learning a totally different programming model can be a challenge for many programmers. Another challenge is that not all components in a complex metagenomics data processing pipeline can be easily ported to Spark due to the lack of corresponding libraries.

4.3 Future Perspectives

I was only able to cover a few scaling strategies for metagenomics analysis in the context of ease of development, robustness, scalability, and efficiency. One might have to combine several strategies, for example, using a single node for development and HPC for large-scale production. When the scale of the analysis exceeds one's on-premises capacity, they can "spillover" to cloud-based solutions for additional capacity.

A significant challenge will remain for scalable computational metagenomics is retaining software talent, in the context of big tech companies are hungry for them. A primary reason why many applications fail to scale up to big data is poor software design. We may continue to rely on unreliable software tools developed by amateurs for a while. Meanwhile, Infrastructure-as-a-service (IAAS), software-as-a-service (SAAS) platforms are reducing the hurdle to adopt scalable technologies. For example, cloud computing technologies make it easy for users to scale up their infrastructure. DataBricks Inc provides Apache Spark as a hosted service with a notebook interface for exploring big data. We may see more cloud-based metagenomics solutions based on these infrastructures and software. Cloud-based analytic systems integrate data management (store, access, and share) and data analysis into one platform, provide flexibility to scale in/out and up/down, and offer user-friendly, consistent, reproducible data pipelines. In the biomedical field there are already such solutions, e.g., Terra (https://app.terra.bio/), which unshackles metagenomics data scientists from the burden of managing hardware and software infrastructures and enable large team collaborations.

Effective scaling also requires close coordination between hardware and software strategies. This may bring future solutions involving the co-design hardware and software. In one of such pioneer studies, researchers enabled FPGA chips to have direct access to the CPU memory for speeding up kmer-based statistics (Haghi *et al.*, 2020). The results showed that co-design outperforms the alternative in both computing and power consumption efficiency.

Chapter 5

Metagenomics Data Quality Improvement

After we obtain the metagenome data from our favorite sequencing technologies, select the best algorithms for the underlying scientific problem, prepare a scalable infrastructure for the large data volume, are we ready for plugging in automatic pipelines to discover novel metagenomics insights? Not quite yet. Almost all types of metagenomic data and metadata contain noise, errors, gaps, and biases. Removing errors and noise, filling in gaps, correct biases in the data, or data wrangling, are probably the least fun part of computational metagenomics. If missed or not done properly, this step can lead to wrong or biased conclusions (although some analysts blame data producers for that). It is almost always necessary to manually explore the data to identify the types and extent of potential quality issues. This step also takes a major part of the manual time in our analysis project. In general, data uncertainty or veracity is a common problem in big data analytics, one of the four "Vs" we discussed in Chapter 4.

The central goal of data quality improvement involves identifying and subsequently removing as many confounding factors as possible to ensure successful downstream analyses. You will not find detailed descriptions of this step in the published literature, yet many metagenomics data analysis workshops spend significant effort in this step. The topic of data quality improvement itself may warrant an entire book about it, here I will discuss some of the most common data quality issues in metagenomics and how to deal with them.

5.1 Removing Common Errors

5.1.1 *Errors in sample metadata and annotation Data*

I discussed the importance of metagenomics metadata in Chapter 2. Like other types of metadata, metagenomics sample metadata is not immune to human errors despite extensive scrutiny. Metadata errors broadly exist in the domain of data science. For instance, a new research by researchers at MIT suggests that labeling errors are prevalent at an average of 3.4%, across all popular datasets used in image recognition machine learning (Northcutt *et al.*, 2021). After these errors were removed, the rank for best models were also changed. As metagenome sequencing projects are carried out in centralized genome sequencing centers or cores, during the processing and pooling of hundreds of samples, some mislabeling is likely. Actually, sample mislabeling is so prevalent in clinical samples that the National Cancer Institute and the Food and Drug Administration launched a computational challenge to the research community to help to detect and correct specimen mislabeling (Boja *et al.*, 2018). There have not been systematic studies of all types of errors in metagenomics sample metadata, but it is conceivable that other types of errors are also prevalent. Unlike the base quality associated with sequencing data, there is no established quality measurement for sample metadata.

As we will see in the next chapters, assembling genomes and annotating them remain challenging despite the rapid improvements in sequencing and computational technologies. These annotation errors are generated at an incredible speed and are propagated more because computational methods rely on them as references (Salzberg, 2019). This type of errors are often difficult to identify, and correcting them itself is the goal of numerous computational metagenomics studies.

5.1.1.1 *Supervised methods for metadata correction*

If we know what to expect in the metadata, or if we have the correct metadata of existing samples, we could use supervised methods to detect and correct errors in metadata for new samples. For example, we can train a machine learning classifier based on the sequencing data to predict sample labels using a set of samples with correct labels. This approach has been demonstrated to be feasible in a recent study, where researchers were able to build either a random forest classifier and a nearest shrunken centroid classifier to learn the true data labels of the intentionally mislabeled samples (Knights *et al.*, 2011). Random forest and nearest centroid are both popular classification methods in machine learning. For readers who are not familar with the nearest centroid classifier, it assigns a new observation with a known class label that its mean (centroid) is closest to. To reduce noise in the observations, as noise is common in metagenomic data, a threshold is also trained to shrink/move class centroids for better accuracy (for a detailed explanation of this method and its application see (Tibshirani *et al.*, 2002). These classifiers can even tolerate a small percentage of labeling errors in the training set, making them quite useful in the realworld settings. The performance of these classifiers, however, starts to decrease when the percent of mislabeled samples in the training set exceeds a certain threshold (over 30%). They did not work well on cases where the data categories are more subtle, either (Knights *et al.*, 2011).

5.1.1.2 *Unsupervised methods for metadata correction*

Alternatively, we could use unsupervised methods to detect potential sample mislabeling or errors in annotations. You may have already been manually visualizing your data with histograms, box plots, and scatter plots to explore the relationships between samples and to identify potential outliers/abnormalities. With a large number of samples, and each sample has many tributes in its metadata, manually exploring these data becomes impractical. Fortunately, anomaly detection is one of the problems in machine learning that have been extensively researched, and there are many algorithms available for us to use. Goldstein and Uchida provided a comprehensive review of these methods in a review (Goldstein and Uchida, 2016). Among the algorithms they compared in their review, k nearest-neighbor (KNN), clustering-based plotting such as clustermap, and one-class SVM classifiers are frequently employed to explore data at the beginning phase of analysis tasks to detect potential errors in metadata. Unsupervised methods can even be used to detect errors in golden standard taxonomy annotations in NCBI, identifying missing or erroneous taxa classification (Wang *et al.*, 2019b). In this unpublished work where I was involved,

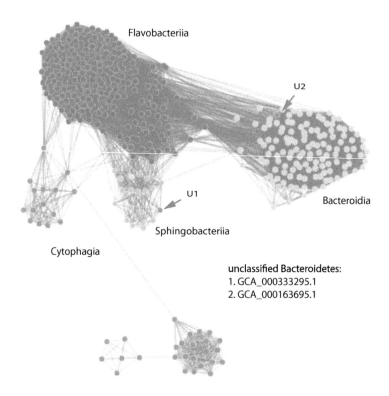

Fig. 5.1 Unsupervised data clustering reveals taxonomic annotation gaps. Using Genome Constellation software (Wang *et al.*, 2019b), bacterial reference genomes from the Bacteroidetes phylum are clustered based on similarity of their sequence composition. Two previously unclassified genomes (U1 and U2) can now be classified at least at the Class level.

we built a graph using the kmer composition of reference bacterial genomes in NCBI and explored their similarities. We found that some of the unclassified genomes may be classified as they are clustered together with the classified genomes, as shown in Figure 5.1.

5.1.2 *Errors in sequence data*

Sequencing technology introduces various errors to the metagenome sequencing data. There are multiple sources that could introduce errors into the sequencing data. Some of the errors are introduced before sequencing, for example, at the PCR amplification step in some library preparation protocols. Some of the errors are introduced during sequencing, either occurred by chance or caused by systematic biases associated with the sequencing technology itself. Short-read sequencing technologies typically have an error rate of approximately 0.1–2% of the bases sequenced, while errors in long-read sequencing technologies typically occur much higher. Some of the errors happen when sequencers misinterpret the signal or when the DNA polymerase incorporates the wrong nucleotide.

To identify errors in the sequencing data, the easiest way is to look at the base quality scores. A quick refresher of what we learned in Chapter 2, genomic sequencers estimate the confidence of each base they called using a PHRED score, Q30 means it's 99.9% sure the base is correct. In the ideal world, we can trust these scores determined by the manufacturer of the sequencing machines. Unfortunately, the scores are subject to various sources of systematic technical error, and they also fail to reflect errors introduced from sources other than the sequencing reactions. Even if we could trust these scores, a 100-gigabase dataset (10^{11} base) with an average quality score of Q30 still leaves us with 10^8, or 100 million erroneous bases!

As the characteristics of sequencing errors derived from different sequencing technologies are different, I will discuss the different strategies that are independent of the base quality score for short-read and long-read data, respectively.

5.1.2.1 *Identifying errors in short reads using Bloom filter*

For short reads, as the error rate is relatively low and the sequencing depth is high, we can afford to filter out data containing errors without worrying about correcting them. We can use the kmer representation of sequencing data and transform the problem of identifying sequencing errors into identifying erroneous kmers. Because the error rate is low, 1–2% for Illumina platforms, and if the errors are random, the probability of an exact erroneous kmer is extremely low, only about $0.25 \times 0.01 \times 0.01 = 0.0000025$, or one in 40,000. In other words, almost all erroneous kmers just happen once. In contrast, in a single-genome sequencing project, a genomic region is often sequenced 50–100 times, the correct kmers would occur 50–100 times on average. Therefore, we can simply count the kmers and remove those occurring only once in the dataset. For metagenomics datasets, however, this practice may unavoidably remove rare species or strains, especially when the community diversity is high or sequencing depth is low. In applications that can tolerate a low percentage of errors, such as mapping reads to reference genomes, error filtering should be skipped. For metagenome assembly, where erroneous kmers lead to branching in the assembly graph, it is essential to remove them before the assembly. Filtering out erroneous kmers can also reduce the data volume. In theory, only 53% of 31-mers are correct given an error rate of 2%, hence removing erroneous kmers can effectively cut the data volume by half.

Counting kmers in a small dataset is easy. We could simply build a hash table with kmers are keys and their counts are values, and pass the sequence data once to get kmers. Doing the same on really large datasets will inevitably run into problems, as the hash table with hundreds of billions of elements would exceed the memory a workstation has. Many computing algorithms have been developed for efficient error filtering, a comprehensive comparison of these methods can be found in a recent review (Mitchell *et al.*, 2020). Here I will only illustrate how a popular data structure that achieves both space and time efficiency.

In computer science, a Bloom filter is a space-efficient probabilistic data structure, conceived by Burton Howard Bloom in 1970 (https://en.wikipedia.org/wiki/Bloom_filter#Distributed_Bloom_filters). It has a uniquely useful feature, that is, it can efficiently test whether or not an element is in a very large set with only a small false positive rate. This feature can be used to distinguish erroneous kmers from the good ones, as the majority of erroneous kmers appear only once in the dataset. To do this, we can construct a Bloom filter to keep track whether or not we have seen a kmer before, and only save that we have seen at least once. We will still have a small number of erroneous kmers that pass through the filter. This is an inherent limitation of Bloom filters, but this small number of false positives, if desired, can be further reduced by implementing additional hash functions.

A Bloom filter with 1% false positive rate and an optimal value of hash size requires only about 9.6 bits per kmer — regardless of the size of the kmer. This space-saving feature can be further improved, as demonstrated in the error-correction tool, Lighter (LIGHTweight ERror corrector, [Song *et al.* (2014)]). Lighter uses a pair of Bloom filters instead of one. The first Bloom filter holds a random sample of all kmers in the sequence. As we discussed above, erroneous kmers are less likely to appear multiple times, therefore, correct kmers are more likely to be sampled. This trick can dramatically decrease the size of the Bloom filter. The other Bloom filter is obtained by passing the input reads a second time through the first filter, and only holds kmers likely to be correct. Finally, the erroneous kmers are corrected during the third pass of the input reads, where a closely matched alternative correct kmer replaces an erroneous one. Because Lighter only uses about a third of the RAM compared to other methods based on Bloom filters, it can hold the entire data structure in RAM instead of relying on disks, which also gives it a speed advantage (Song *et al.*, 2014).

5.1.2.2 *Long-read error correction*

In the above short-read base error correction process, kmers are assumed to contain at most one error. This is a reasonable assumption given the overall 99% base accuracy of Illumina sequencing. This assumption does not hold for long-read datasets, however. Given a 15% error rate, fewer than 1% of 31-mers contain no errors, while 96% contain more than one error. Applying the above methods based on Bloom filter would filter out the vast majority of the data. We need to correct the errors so that the dataset becomes usable, but we would need different algorithms or strategies for long-read error correction.

There are three main strategies depending on whether or not we have a matching short-read dataset from the same sample. If we do, we could align the short reads to the long reads and use the consensus of the aligned short reads to patch and polish the long reads. Alternatively, we could also assemble the short reads into contigs, and then align the contigs to the long reads and use the consensus (contig) sequence to correct the long reads. If matching short-read data is not available, we could align the long reads to one another to derive the consensus sequences. Figure 5.2 illustrates these three strategies.

Among the three, long-read only (Strategy 3) requires high coverage for effective error correction, which is a disadvantage as long-read sequencing is relatively more expensive. Correction aided by short reads can achieve better correction, especially when the long-read sequencing depth is low. Assembly-based methods (Strategy 2) have a

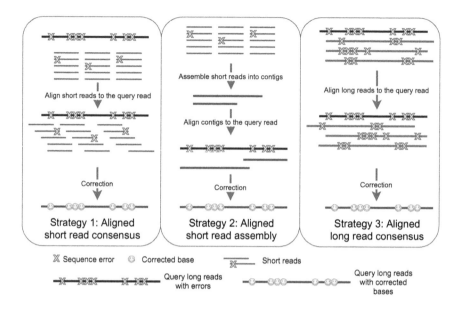

Fig. 5.2   Long read base error correction strategies.

scalability advantage on large data sets than alignment-based methods (Strategy 1). While a comparison of the methods based on the above strategies can be found in a recent review (Zhang *et al.*, 2020), a word of caution about these base error correction methods in the context of metagenomics: we might remove strain-level divergence as a consequence of error correction. This could happen during both short and long-read correction processes, where we correct the sequences from a rare strain to those from its more abundant sisters. If strain diversity is the question of interest, we will have to recover the diversity from the uncorrected reads, or forgo error correction altogether.

5.2 Missing Data Imputation

Missing data is everywhere in genomics studies: unmeasured modification status in epigenomic datasets, missing genotype information in genome-wide association studies, and dropout events in single-cell RNA-sequencing experiments (scRNA-seq). The missing data issue is worse in metagenomics. Due to the limited sequencing depth, some rare species may be out of luck in the random sampling game, and their abundance appears to be zero ("false zero"). We can ramp up our sequencing efforts to increase their chances to be seen, but after a certain point we hit "the law of diminishing returns", as more sequencing simply produces more data from the abundant members of the community. As a result, the species abundance matrix we obtained could be very sparse, containing a large proportion of zeros. Some of them are true zeros, i.e., the species does not exist in this community. Some of them must be false zeros, for example, we observed a member in some of the biological replicates but not in others, or a member appears in some of the samples but not in others in a time-series experiment.

From a metagenomics aspect, the missing data issue impairs analyses such as deferentially enrichment taxon analysis to identify taxa that exhibit different abundances among samples. The difference in the number of zeros between two samples can produce artificial statistical significance. From an algorithmic aspect, missing data can lead to null values (e.g., during log-transformation) that may break the analysis software.

There are a number of ways to handle null values, including deleting rows with null values, replacing null values with the mean/median/mode derived from all replicates, replacing null values with a new category (eg. unknown), or predicting the values using machine learning. There are several imputation tools developed for other types of genomics data that may be applied to metagenomics data. For example, softImpute iteratively fills in missing data using expectation maximization (EM)-like algorithms (Mazumder *et al.*, 2010). Many imputation methods have achieved great successes in scRNA-seq, could the same imputation methods also be applied to metagenomics data? Jiang et al. (Jiang *et al.*, 2020) argued that they are not likely suitable for metagenomics data due to three reasons. First, the diverse types of metagenomics data are much more complex than scRNA-seq data, as they include metadata such as phylogeny that are not easily imputed. Second, while multiple single-cell data from the same tissue or type are presumed similar, thereby enabling imputation based on one another. This presumption is not applicable to microbial communities. Instead, the structure of a microbial community are more heterogeneous: multiple strains from the same species, and multiple cells from the same strain are more diverse. Third, the smaller sample size of metagenomic datasets excludes them from being suitable for deep learning-based imputation methods. To overcome these challenges, the authors proposed a new software, mImpute, that can impute on three types of data (sequence, taxa, and metadata) to effectively reduce false zeros (Mazumder *et al.*, 2010).

5.3 Remove Irrelevant Data: Data Filtering

Besides missing information, almost all metagenomics sequencing data is plagued with extra information as well. As data from other NGS experiments, metagenomics sequence data can contain sequencing adapters or control sequences that have not been automatically removed, common lab contaminants that get into the data during library construction and sequencing processes. These extra data should be removed by comparing to the known adapter sequences or known references of the contaminants. For host-associated communities, the data can contain a large proportion of genomic data of the host. Unless we are studying host-microbe interactions, we may also want to remove the contaminated host data.

If the sequencing library has undergone PCR amplification, it is also necessary to remove the duplicates resulted from PCR, as they may confound count-based statistics such as community composition or gene expression level in metatranscriptomics studies. For metatranscriptomic sequencing data, ribosomal RNA sequences are often not desirable and need to be filtered out.

Some of the irrelevant data are project-specific as the experimental design can greatly confound data filtering. These often can be identified or removed if we know our expectations or if controls are available. For example, increasing throughput in DNA sequencers has enabled multiplexing, a routine practice to sequence several samples in one sequencing run. Data derived from each sample can be distinguished by a sample-specific short oligo "barcode". If the "demultiplex" step has not completely removed the barcode sequences, we may have to implement extra steps to remove them. Sometime "barcode cross-talk" can occur, where some data of one sample can be assigned to a different one because their barcode sequences are similar. This problem is much pronounced in single-cell genome sequencing projects, and we will revisit this issue and potential solutions later in Chapter 9.

5.4 Control Noise and Biases

After the above extensive data filtering and error correcting, now it is time to combat statistical and biological noise and biases. For people who are familiar with transcriptomics analyses, microbial taxa count data share many characteristics with the gene count data in skewed-distribution, zero-inflation, and over-dispersion. The species abundance distribution in many communities can be highly skewed, instead of a symmetrical normal distribution. A few dominant species are highly abundant, while the vast majority of other species have very few counts, leading to a distribution with a very long tail. As we discussed earlier in the imputation of missing data, many rare species would have zero counts due to the limited sequence depth, or we would have a zero-inflation problem. Because of the inherent biological variability among samples, counts of the same species between different replicates could vary greatly, with abundant species varying much more (over-dispersion). These noises and biases lead to challenges in downstream statistical analyses. Not just taxa count data, the sequence data can carry biases, too. For example, it is well known that Illumina short-read sequencing biases against genomic regions or species with extreme GC-content, so that AT- or GC-rich regions or genomes have poor sequencing coverage.

Fortunately, several methods have been developed to combat these noises and biases. Data normalization is a standard process to transform the data to control noise and biases. We can scale the taxa counts by dividing the total read count of a sample followed by a log transformation so that we can compare the counts across samples at the same scale. We can standardize the counts so that it has a mean of zero and a standard deviation of 1. We can also normalize the counts between replicates so that their distributions have a similar shape, as this is assumed by some statistical methods. The choice of normalization methods are highly dependent on the underlying data and the pertained scientific question, I will not go into details here, but do want to point you to an excellent review about this topic (Calle, 2019).

Besides biological variations between individual samples, an often overlooked complication in genomics studies is batch effects, or variations among different batches of samples, or different studies, introduced by laboratory, experiment/computation protocol, and personnel differences. This becomes one of the major reasons why metagenomics findings could not be replicated among different studies. Normalization technique does not effectively remove batch effects, as it corrects the global data distribution instead of specific subsets of the data affected by batch effects. In metagenomics, the effect of batch effects has not been systematically studied, but several studies have uncovered that they can exert a major influence on, and in some cases account for the main findings (Randall *et al.*, 2019; de Goffau *et al.*, 2021). During the exploratory phase of data analysis, unsupervised methods such as principal component analysis or hierarchical clustering may reveal whether the major differences are due to true biology or batch. If the samples are clustered strongly by batches (lab, protocol, study, processing time, etc), it is an indication that strong batch effects exist, and they must be accounted for before a conclusion could be made.

5.5 Pitfalls in Metagenomics Data Improvement

We often need to explore the data to get to gain some insight before laying out a quality improvement plan. This step can become a lengthy process in many analysis projects. At this step, it is crucial to start with a small fraction of the data, work out the strategy first with a small amount of computing resources, and then apply the strategy to the big dataset with the desired computing resources.

There is an old saying "better underdone than overdone", this should similarly apply to the data quality improvement process for three reasons. First, once the data is filtered out, it is harder to get them back. It is advised to only fix the relevant data quality issues that confound a particular analysis task. If we decide an additional filtering step is needed for another analysis task, we would have the option to further filter the data. Second, filtering itself may take a considerable amount of computing resources. For example, to remove potential contaminants, we would search the data against a large collection of potential contaminant genomes. Finally, some of the steps, such as error correction and normalization, could introduce unintended changes to the data. For example, kmer-based error correction has been proved very successful in single-genome projects, but it is not known whether or not this process masks the information of subspecies or strains. In theory, we could have corrected the data from a relatively rare strain to its more abundant sister strain.

Many of the common data quality issues nowadays are handled by automatic QA/QC pipelines. While these automatic pipelines are great for generic purposes, we need to keep in mind that sometimes they are not complete, and can remove critical information required for our project-specific information. For example, most of the QA/QC pipelines run in batches, so they do not remove batch effects, and in some cases different versions of these pipelines can actually create batch effects. In addition, ribosomal RNAs are typically removed from meta-transcriptomics data, but these data could be used for getting taxonomic information about the community, a topic we will delve into in the next chapter.

Chapter 6

Exploring Community Diversity:
Taxonomic Analyses

By now, probably only a caveman does not know that one needs a diverse microbiome to be healthy, as the media has done a great job associating the human microbiome with human health. We are told to have a diverse diet to increase our microbiome diversity, and we need it for the health of our immune system to defend infections. Lack of diversity in the gut microbiome can lead to obesity. Microbiome diversity also underlies many chronic inflammatory diseases, such as psoriasis in the skin and colorectal cancer in the colon. A baby inherits its microbiome from its mother during natural birth, but a baby delivered through cesarean section may lack a healthy microbiome diversity to start with ... There are numerous studies on microbiome diversity, and experts are hotly debating what consists a healthy microbiome. These debates were summarized by a science journalist, Michael Eisenstein, in a commentary published in Nature Outlook on January 29th, 2020 (https://www.nature.com/articles/d41586-020-00193-3).

Studying diversity is one of the most important questions in ecology. Microdiversity, a new discipline, did not have any theory to begin with, so it had to borrow from macrodiversity, its close sibling. The diversity of a community provides a low resolution of the community function, and in some cases the diversity itself is used as a proxy of community function, e.g., gut microbiome diversity is an indicator of human gut health. Changes in diversity can be correlated with microbial dynamics to identify drivers and make predictions of community function. Factors that increase niche availability, such as diverse resources or increased niche area, or that limit microbial growth, such as frequent disturbances or chronically extreme conditions, are expected to drive diversity in opposite directions. Understanding microbial diversity and the factors driving their changes not only provides insights into human health, but also presents a unique opportunity for us to understand the interplay between microbes and our environment, an issue becoming more urgent given the current trend of climate change.

What is diversity anyway? In this chapter, I will introduce the concept of microdiversity and methods to accurately measure it.

6.1 What is Microdiversity?

When we talk about the microdiversity of a community, we may refer to two different things depending on context. Taxonomic diversity refers to the diversity measured at the species level, while functional diversity refers to diversity at the gene or pathway level.

6.1.1 *Taxonomic diversity*

Taxonomic diversity measures how many types of microbes or taxa are within a sample or community. Taxonomic diversity can be measured at the level of many taxonomic ranks (superkingdom, phylum, class, order, family, genus, and species), and species is the most commonly used. Very often, operational taxonomic units (OTUs, I will explain this later) are used in the literature, which is equivalent to species.

We are concerned with two common properties of a community in the context of taxonomic diversity: how many species are in the community and how evenly they are distributed. The former is also referred as community composition or richness, and the latter is also referred as community structure. The measured diversity within a sample/community is also called alpha diversity, to be distinguished between sample diversity (beta diversity). The concepts of the two diversity metrics, as well as within- and between-sample diversity, are illustrated in Figure 6.1.

6.1.1.1 *Within sample diversity indices: alpha diversity*

In practice, the observed richness in a sample is likely an underestimate of the true community richness, as rare species are harder to

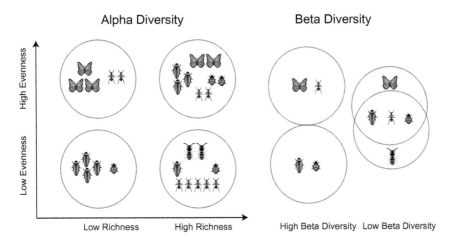

Fig. 6.1 Alpha diversity vs Beta diversity. The diversity within a sample or a community is called alpha diversity. The diversity between different samples or communities is called beta diversity. In the illustration, the number of different species (richness) is shown on the x-axis, and the species evenness is shown on the y-axis. Each circle represents a sample. Different insects (bugs) are used to represent different microbes, as sometimes the microbes are also called "bugs".

detect given a limited sampling depth. In a community with high richness, the probability that a species will be observed more than once can be low. Conversely, in a low diversity community, the probability that a species will be observed more than once will be higher, and more abundant species will be observed multiple times in a sample. Is it possible to count the unobserved one? This is actually also a common problem faced in macroecology studies, and Chao et al. developed a good estimator, called Chao1 index(Chao, 1984). Chao1 index is also borrowed by microecologists for estimating the number of unobserved members of a community. Assuming the number of species that appear only once in the sample is f_1 and the number of species that appear twice is f_2, and the true community richness $\hat{R}$ can be estimated from the observed richness R using the following Chao1 index formula:

$$\hat{R} = R + \frac{f_1(f_1 - 1)}{(2f_2 + 1)} \tag{1}$$

Chao1 index assumes that the number of observations for taxa has a Poisson distribution and it corrects for variance by adding a term to count the unobserved taxa. When $f_1 \gg 1$ and $f_2 \gg 1$, the term can also be approximated as $\frac{f_1^2}{2f_2}$. If the majority of the species have a single count, then the Chao1 estimated richness would be large, with a maximum value of R^2 when all species in the sample are singletons. This index is particularly useful for datasets skewed toward low-abundance species. Using simulated datasets, Hughes et al. found the Chao1 index is a reasonably good estimator of the true richness over alternative methods (Hughes *et al.*, 2001).

To measure how evenly the species are distributed within a community, a commonly used diversity metric is the Shannon diversity index. This metric weighs the number of observed species by their relative evenness data. To calculate Shannon diversity index, we first calculate the relative proportion p_i of a species i, and then multiply it by its natural logarithm $\log p_i$. The resulting product is summed across all R species in the sample, and multiplied by -1:

$$H = - \sum_{i=1}^{R} p_i \log p_i \tag{2}$$

As you can see from the above equation, the Shannon diversity index (H) of a community increases with richness (R). When Richness is fixed, H reaches a maximum when the proportions of all species are equal.

From an evolutionary perspective, diversity can also be measured by phylogenetic diversity (Faith, 1992). Phylogenetic diversity is a metric based on phylogeny, defined by the combined branch length of all species within the community on a phylogenetic tree that span the members of the set. This metric is not only a quantitative measure of the total amount of species diversity within a community, but also can measure the different consequences of losing some species. In the illustration in Figure 6.2, losing the sole member in a deep brunch can lead to a collapse in overall diversity.

There are a few other alpha diversity indices that are used in the literature. For an in-depth understanding of these indices and how they are used, please refer this review (Finotello *et al.*, 2018).

6.1.1.2 *Between sample diversity indices: beta diversity*

Unlike alpha diversity, beta diversity is a metric to highlight the taxonomic difference between a pair of samples. This metric will be useful when we compare two samples, for example, to see how the microbes react after we apply a physical stress.

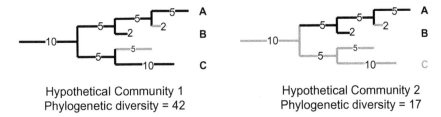

Hypothetical Community 1
Phylogenetic diversity = 42

Hypothetical Community 2
Phylogenetic diversity = 17

Fig. 6.2 Phylogenetic diversity. It is defined as the combined branch length of all species within a community on a phylogenetic tree that span the members of the set. The branches in gray represent species that are not present in the community. The numbers represent relative phylogenetic distance. Losing a member from the community (C in community 1) with deep brunch can lead to a large decrease of the overall phylogenetic diversity.

Like alpha diversity, several metrics have been developed for beta diversity. The simplest Jaccard distance ignores species abundance and just uses the number of matched/mismatched species, weighing each species equally (Figure 6.1). UniFrac distance is a commonly used metric used for beta diversity (Lozupone *et al.*, 2007). It has both a weighted variant that accounts for abundance and an unweighted variant that only accounts for presence/absence. UniFrac is based on phylogenetic distance. After all taxa in both samples are placed on a phylogenetic tree, each branch is classified as either "shared" or "unique" according to its leading to a shared taxon from both samples. The UniFrac distance between a pair of samples is then calculated as the unique fraction of the total branch.

If we have many samples, we would end up with a pairwise Jaccard or UniFrac distance matrix. We can then visually explore the relationship among these samples by a technique called principal coordinates analysis (PCoA). PCoA is one of the ordination methods to represent sample relationships as faithfully as possible in a low-dimensional space.

It is worth noting that the PCoA introduced here is related to Principal Component Analysis (PCA) that you might be already familiar with. While both are used to explore sample relationships, there is an important distinction between the two. In PCoA, we perform ordination with a distance matrix as input. In PCA, on the other hand, we start with a sample-OTU frequency matrix as input, compute the Euclidean distance matrix between samples, and then run PCoA. Therefore, PCA is a special case of PCoA. Since we prefer to use the distance matrix specifically developed for beta diversity, PCoA is much more common than PCA in microecology studies.

QIIME2 is a software package that supports the calculation of most of the diversity indices. Here is a post showing how to run the commands: https://forum.qiime2.org/t/alpha-and-beta-diversity-explanations-and-commands/2282

6.1.1.3 *The effect of sampling depth in calculating diversity*

The depth of sampling, or sequencing coverage in the metagenome sequencing context, can affect at least two aspects of diversity measurement. We have discussed the underestimation of the true richness using the observed richness. In addition, the sampling depth also confounds our comparison of the richness between a pair of samples. Suppose we sequence 1 million reads from a community and count the number of occurrences of each taxon. We would like to compare those from the same community that a colleague sequenced at an earlier time point, to see whether or not the richness changes between these two time points. For the earlier time point, she only sequenced 0.5 million reads. We are likely to observe a higher richness number in our sample because our sequence depth is twice as high as hers and we can detect more rare species. How do we make a fair comparison?

We could simply randomly sample each sample to the same depth before computing the richness index. To reduce the randomness associated with sampling, we could repeat the same process multiple times and take an average. Actually, there is a more statistical robust way to do this. We could produce a rarefraction curve, a technique also first developed for macroecology, to plot the average of richness at different sampling depths (Sanders, 1968). Figure 6.3 illustrates three rarefraction curves. With rarefraction analysis, we can see sample A has a similar diversity index to sample B despite their sequencing depth is dramatically different, while sample C has much higher diversity.

After the sampling depth goes beyond a certain point, our ability to detect rare species stops increasing, and the curve reaches a plateau. Therefore, rarefaction is not only used for comparing the diversity between different samples, it can also be used to determine whether

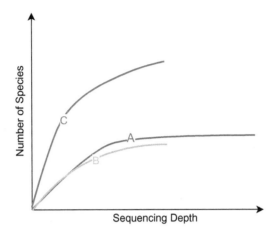

Fig. 6.3   Rarefraction curve illustration.

or not sufficient sampling has been reached in a given sample, based on whether or not the curve is converged.

6.1.2 *Functional diversity*

Taxonomic composition alone can only provide a rough estimate of community function. Identification of genes, gene families, and specific metabolic pathways can understand the functional capabilities of the community. Gut microbiomes of very different compositions can have very similar functional gene profiles among different individuals. A 2009 study found that different human individuals share an extensive, identifiable 'core microbiome' at the gene, rather than at the species level (Turnbaugh *et al.*, 2009). The same diversity indices used for taxonomic diversity can be applied to functional diversity, by replacing species with gene families or metabolic pathways. We will learn how to identify genes and pathways using computational approaches in Chapter 7.

6.2 Taxonomic Classification in Metagenomics

We have discussed diversity metrics without mentioning how we derive taxa from metagenome sequence data. From an algorithmic perspective, taxonomy involves grouping similar organisms (functionally or genetically) into groups to form taxa (clustering) and assigning new organisms to an existing or known taxon (classification). Driven by experimental technology development, the taxonomy system has evolved from morphology-based (microscopy), to molecular-based (16s rRNA), and finally to whole genome-based. The process of assigning taxa scientific names is called nomenclature. In nomenclature, the "two-term naming system" is used to name a species, which is composed of two parts, a generic name identifying the genus and a specific name identifying the species within the genus. The names were intended to both label species and carry some biological meaning. However, the taxonomic nomenclature can be ambiguous. For example, some of the species are named after their morphology. *Bacillus subtilis* (Bacillus in Latin means "stick" while subtilis being the Latin for "fine") was used to describe a group of bacteria found on grass whose cells look fine sticks under the microscope. Clearly, there are so many stick-like bacteria that can be totally unrelated in either function or phylogeny to Bacillus. For now, let us just keep in mind that the scientific names are just labels of taxa. Here, we are going to focus on taxa formation or classification, i.e., forming new taxa or inferring the presence of known taxa given metagenomic sequence data. More specifically, we will deal with the problem of predicting the taxa of the microbial species in a community, with their genomes may or may not have been assembled.

We mentioned at the beginning of the book that a large percentage of the species we find in a metagenome project are often unknown. Therefore, discovering novel taxa is one of the main tasks of computational metagenomics. A recent study surveyed datasets from the human microbiome and recovered thousands of potential new species (Pasolli *et al.*, 2019). Our current understanding of the scale of microorganism diversity is probably much underappreciated, as an experiment that overcomes sampling biases by obtaining samples from a diverse environments revealed (Rinke *et al.*, 2013).

Suppose we have a species whose genome is assembled from the metagenome data (we will cover the assembly process in Chapter 8), how do we know whether or not it represents a new taxa group? The process is called phylogenetic inference, or placing the species on the phylogenetic tree to determine its evolutionary history with a set of related species.

From an algorithmic perspective, formulating the problem this way can effectively model it as a supervised machine learning problem: Given a set of reference species with known taxonomic labels, predict the label of new genomes. As other machine learning problems, we would need features (or attributes) of a genome for training a model and making predictions. As both references and queries are genomic sequences, the taxonomy classification can also be modeled as a sequence similarity search problem, i.e., finding the best match of a sequence in a reference database (and assuming the taxonomic information of the target).

6.2.1 *Super features: phylogenetic markers*

Early taxonomy classification of microorganisms was based on qualitative or qualitative morphology differences such as those in cell shape. In the early 1970s, Carl Woese (1928-2012) realized that the sequence of 16S ribosomal RNA (rRNA) serves as a much more precise and stable marker for bacteria phylogeny. By analyzing the 16S rRNA of some "extremophiles" that live at temperatures up to 100°C, Woese discovered Archaea, a third domain of life that is distantly related to bacteria and eukaryotes. Since then, 16S rRNA became a universal marker for prokaryotes, and 18S rRNA for eukaryotes. Using 16S/18S rRNA gene (rDNA) as a super feature, the taxonomic classification problem becomes searching a query rRNA sequence against a database of labeled rRNA sequences. In the following, we will discuss 16S/18S rRNA sequencing and then briefly review rDNA databases.

6.2.1.1 *16S/18S sequencing*

Targeted amplification sequencing (TAS) of 16S/18S rRNA is currently one of the most used strategies for the identification and quantification of microorganisms in a community. The 16S/18S rRNA gene contains regions that are highly conserved between species and regions that are highly variable or discriminative between species. Polymerase chain reaction (PCR) primers can be designed from conserved regions to amplify one or more variable regions and subsequently sequence them using high-throughput sequencing technologies such as Illumina. The size of the whole 16S and 18S rRNA genes are around 1.5 kb and 1.9 kb, respectively, which are much larger than the read length from the short-read sequencing technology(less than 300 bases). One or more shorter variable regions of the gene are therefore targeted for sequencing. The biggest advantage of TAS is its low sequencing cost, as only a tiny fraction of a genome is sequenced, and with a fixed sequencing budget one can get better coverage of the taxonomic diversity. 16S/18S-based TAS sequencing has become a method of choice to survey the taxonomic diversity of complex microbial communities (taxonomic profiling), as it is sensitive, qualitative, and quantitative.

In addition to the sequencing errors in Illumina-sequenced amplicon data, PCR also introduces errors, both needing to be distinguished from the true variations observed among different species. Given the presence of these confounding errors, how could one reliably quantify each of the species in the community? There are two common strategies: OTU-based and ASV-based. In the first strategy, sequencing errors can be addressed by clustering the reads into operational taxonomic units (OTUs) using a predefined sequence identity threshold (typically 97%). In TAS, OTUs refer to a cluster of similar sequence variants of the 16S/18S rDNA sequences. With the risk of merging several real sequences into one, a consensus sequence from each cluster contains much fewer errors. Each OTU represents a taxonomic unit of a microbial species (sometimes a genus when a lower sequence identity threshold is used). In contrast to the clustering strategy in OTU-based analysis, the Amplicon Sequence Variant (ASV) strategy uses an error model to compute the statistical confidence of a given read at a given frequency that is not due to sequencer error. ASV has the advantage over OTU in that it uses exact sequences instead of consensus ones (or "fuzzy" sequences), allowing much higher resolution (at strain or substrain levels) for taxa identification. For a detail explanation of these strategies, please refer to this blog (https://www.zymoresearch. com/blogs/blog/microbiome-informatics-otu-vs-asv).

There are a few limitations of 16S/18S-based taxonomic profiling. First, primers designed using conserved regions can have biases, as they could favorably amplify some species but unfavorably amplify others. These primers will only target prokaryotes or eukaryotes, but not viruses and phages. Second, as only shorter variable regions of the gene are targeted due to the short sequencing length, the resolution of this technology can be significantly compromised, especially at species level (Johnson *et al.*, 2019; Jeong *et al.*, 2021), urging the need to switch to long-read sequencing technologies to target the whole gene.

6.2.1.2 *Ribosomal RNA databases*

Reads or OTU consensus sequences derived from 16S/18S rDNA genes are mapped to known rRNA databases to be assigned to known taxa, and their number is used to calculate the abundance of each taxon. Among the rRNA databases, SILVA, RDP, and Greengenes are the most popular ones.

The SILVA database (https://www.arb-silva.de/) is a manually curated database that includes 16S/18S rRNA sequences for all three domains of life (Bacteria, Archaea, and Eukarya). It is the most widely used database in 16S/18S-based taxonomic classification analysis. The latest release of SILVA (138.1 as of August 27, 2020) contains 2,224,740 total and 510,508 nonredundant 16S/18S rRNA reference sequences. Besides the large collection of reference sequences, SILVA also offers several related software tools as well as comprehensive data analysis services.

The Ribosomal database project (RDP, https://rdp.cme.msu.edu/) curates 16S rRNA (Bacteria and Archaea) and 28S rRNA (Fungi) sequences. The latest release, RDP Release 11 Update 5 (September 30, 2016), contains 3,356,809 16S rRNAs and 125,525 Fungal 28S rRNAs.

The Greengenes database (https://greengenes.lbl.gov/) is dedicated to Bacteria and Archaea. Although Greengenes is still included in some metagenomic analyses packages, it has not been updated since 2017.

6.2.2 *Features based on whole-genome statistics*

16S/18S sequences are considered by many microbiologists as the "molecular clock" of evolution. However, this clock seems to run at a slightly different speed among different phylogenetic groups, and organisms belonging to closely related yet distinct species may have very similar 16S/18S sequences if the rDNAs evolve slower than the other genomic regions. A common practice in 16S/18S-based taxonomic analysis is grouping rRNA sequences into OTUs at the 97% sequence identity level. This threshold is considered the golden standard for distinguishing species. The ideal threshold cutoff has not been extensively researched, for example, a systematic evaluation of the false discovery rate under it, until recently(Rodriguez-R *et al.*, 2018). A more stringent threshold, 98.5% 16S rRNA sequence identity cutoff, was proposed to be more accurate. Even at this threshold, the 16S rRNA gene-based, one-size-fits-all approach still underestimates species diversity by ~12%, compared with the features based on genome-based statistics discussed below.

As in typical machine learning methods, we can include more features to improve taxonomic classification accuracy. These features include Average Nucleotide Identity (ANI), Average Amino Acid Identity (AAI), and Single Copy Genes (SCG).

6.2.2.1 *ANI/AAI*

ANI and AAI are genome-based metrics. The ANI is defined as the average nucleotide identity among all shared genes between two genomes (Konstantinidis and Tiedje, 2005). Similarly, AAI is the average amino acid identity between the two genomes. Calculating ANI/AAI involves first identifying homologous protein pairs between the two genomes, and then the pairs are aligned and their identity averaged to obtain ANI or AAI. ANI gives better resolution than AAI for closely related species (at the species or genus level), while AAI can be applied to remotely related species beyond the genus level.

Genome-based statistics provide more accurate metrics for taxonomic diversity, in contrast to 16S rRNA gene-based metrics that likely underestimate species richness by at least 10 to 15% (Rodriguez-R *et al.*, 2018). They should also be more robust, as these statistics are derived from many genes rather than a single one, effects such as recent horizontal gene transfer (also known as lateral gene transfer, which is the nonsexual movement of genetic information between genomes instead of vertically through inheritance) should be minimized. As many genomes assembled from metagenome datasets (Chapter 8) or derived from single-cell metagenomics (Chapter 9) are

incomplete and often lack ribosomal genes, ANI/AAI metrics are particularly suited for taxonomic analysis in metagenomics.

The downside of genome-based metrics is that they require more
computation to calculate. Calculating ANI/AAI for a large number of
genomes is very computational expensive, as all-vs-all alignments have
quadratic time complexity, that is, the computing time quadruples as
the number of genomes doubles. For example, JGI's IMG/M database
contains over 90,000 genomes as of May 2021, and it will require over
8 billion comparisons to compute ANI/AAI for the entire dataset.

Several algorithms have been developed to scale up ANI/AAI computation. If we use the similarity of kmer frequencies between two
genomes to approximate their ANI, then we could borrow existing
algorithms from the big data world, as this problem is analogous to
comparing two web pages based on word frequencies. MinHash is
such an algorithm applied to ANI calculation and the program based
on it, Mash, achieves several orders of magnitude of speedup over
Blast-based methods (Ondov *et al.*, 2016). The speed comes with a
cost, though. As other kmer-based approaches, Mash is very sensitive to mutations. The number of shared kmers dramatically decreases
as the two species become more divergent, and the statistics become
less reliable. To overcome this problem, FastANI (Jain *et al.*, 2018)
uses a minimizer-based MashMap algorithm to align more divergent sequence segments between two genomes, while maintaining
high speed, up to three orders of magnitude faster than Blast-based
methods.

While ANI/AAI-based metrics can quickly estimate the similarity
between two genomes, they fail to consider the percent of shared
genes. In an extreme case, two genomes share a single, identical gene
(say, due to a recent horizontal gene transfer event) but nothing else,
and their ANI/AAI would be 100%. Therefore, in practice an "Alignment Fraction" (AF), or the proportion of genes shared, is also considered. Only after AF exceeds a predefined threshold, the ANI/AAI metrics would be considered.

6.2.2.2 *Multiple phylogenetic markers*

Having assembled genomes also enables methods that consider multiple phylogenetic markers to overcome the limitations of a single

low-abundance species (metagenomics perspective) and the exponential growth of reference databases (data engineering perspective). The largest challenge, however, is the lack of ability to detect and characterize unknown species, a common problem for all supervised classification methods. The quick expansion of the reference database, combined with future development of unsupervised approaches, may alleviate or solve this problem.

It is worth noting that the presence of a microorganism in a community, or its abundance, does not directly translate to its importance to the community. This is why functional diversity is often preferred over taxonomic diversity. To identify these "important" species such as those carrying unique metabolic capabilities, researchers often adopt enrichment methods to artificially increase their proportions in the sample. For example, to limit the analysis to the active portion of microbes, but not the inactive or dead microbes, stable isotopes could be used to label the active proliferating cells and subsequently capture and sequence them. This technology is called stable isotope probing (SIP), and it can be used to label both DNA or RNA to enrich actively replicating or transcribing cells, respectively (reviewed in [Singer *et al.* (2017)]).

Chapter 7

Functional Metagenomics: Gene and Pathway-Based Analyses

Every microorganism, however small, encodes a full set of genetic algorithms that ensure their ability to survive in and adapt to the unpredictable environment. They rely on various genes and pathways that provide unique metabolic capabilities. Functional metagenomics involves the identification of genes and pathways in a metagenome dataset and the annotate of their function. Functional metagenomics not only addresses the fundamental question in metagenomics: "what do they do?", but also provides a deep understanding of community diversity, as taxonomic similar organisms such as strains within a species can have dramatic different functions. For example, most *Escherichia coli* (*E. coli*) strains are normal constituents of our gut microbiome that provide us nutrients such as vitamins, but a small number of strains are pathogenic and cause diseases from mild to severe bloody diarrhea. Discoveries in functional metagenomics also greatly expanded the repertoire of potential microbial natural products that have potential biomedical or industrial properties, a process called microbial bioprospecting. According to a report that catalogs the small molecule drugs used for cancer in the last 30 years, 74.8%, are either natural products or their "mimics" (Newman and Cragg, 2012).

In this chapter, we will review various computational strategies to identify genes and pathways and predict their function. Readers need to be aware that functional metagenomics is also carried out by functional screening based on biochemical activity, which is an experimental approach that relies on the construction and high-throughput screening of metagenomic DNA libraries (Lam *et al.*, 2015). Experimental approaches had been a predominant strategy for functional metagenomics before the birth of high-throughput sequencing. Here we will not discuss the experimental approaches involved to discover new functions or validate functional predictions, neither will we cover the genetic or biochemical engineering involved to improve the biochemical properties of microbial natural products. An in-depth review of these topics can be found in a recent publication (Robinson *et al.*, 2021).

Similar to the taxonomic analyses we discussed in the last chapter, the goal of functional analyses also has two folds: to discover new functions encoded by new genes, gene families, or metabolic pathways; and to profile diverse functions of a community and study their changes between conditions, spatial or temporal changes.

7.1 Gene Discovery

The concept of genes was proposed by Gregor Mendel, the "Father of Genetics" in 1966. In 1972, Walter Fiers and his team at the Laboratory of Molecular Biology of the University of Ghent (Ghent, Belgium) sequenced the first gene, the Bacteriophage MS2 coat protein. Powered by next-generation sequencing and gene prediction algorithms, it is now possible to determine the entire set of genes in an organism, large or small. For instance, the human genome is estimated to carry between 25,000 to 30,000 protein-coding genes, while *E. coli* carries about 4,000.

It is not straightforward to determine the full set of genes encoded by a microbial community, however, especially those with high species richness and uneven species abundance. Limited by the sequencing depth, genes from rare species are often missed from detection. By combining multiple samples, one could potentially increase the chance to observe genes from rare species, as rare species from one sample may not be so rare in another, or they become less rare in the combined dataset. This strategy has begun to reveal the enormous functional diversity encoded by microbial communities. In a recent study, Braden Tierney at Harvard Medical School and his colleagues analyzed a large cohort of 3,655 human oral or gut metagenomic samples and found a staggering functional diversity (Tierney *et al.*, 2019). 46 million genes were found in this study, among which more than 50% are uniquely tied to individual people. As the observed genes may still represent a small fraction of the total function diversity, the team estimated that the total number of genes in the collective human microbiome could be around 232 million! This prediction is supported by the human gut microbiome meta-study where over 280,000 genomes were analyzed (Almeida *et al.*, 2021), as over 171 million unique proteins were found. This diversity is just about the human-associated microbial communities, and the entire gene repertoire encoded by the earth microbiome is probably an astronomical number. One of the online genome databases, JGI's Integrated Microbial Genomes and Microbiomes (IMG/M), recorded over 63.8 billion genes as of April, 2021 — we should still be at the dawn of discovering microbial genes.

There are two main strategies to discover genes from a metagenome dataset. Both requires assembly, a process that pieces together short reads, either at the nucleotide level or at the protein level. Both can produce a catalog of genes for functional diversity, and gene abundances in each sample can be found by mapping of reads to the gene catalog to infer functional composition.

7.1.1 *Discover genes based on metagenome assembly*

I will devote the next chapter to discuss metagenome assembly. Here, at a high level, one can employ state-of-the-art assemblers to assemble the short reads based on the de Bruijn graph. We briefly discuss the de Bruijn graph in Chapter 3: it uses kmers as edges and their overlaps as nodes. The traversal of such graphs obtains contigs, many of which are long enough to contain one or more genes. And then a gene prediction program is applied to these contigs to predict genes, based on either their similarity to existing genes or via preestablished gene models. Similarity-based methods are useful to discover genes that have significant homology to genes in the reference databases, and they are the method of choice to identify noncoding genes including tRNA and 16/18s rRNA genes for taxonomic analyses. However, because the majority of protein-coding genes from a metagenomic dataset do not have known homologs in our limited database, the *ab initio* gene prediction, or gene prediction using gene models is the major driving force that fuels the exponential growth in gene numbers.

Prokaryotic protein coding genes have common sequence features, including structure features such as open reading frames (ORFs) and ribosomal binding sites (RBSs), and composition features such as GC-content and codon usage statistics. Various machine learning models are trained based on these sequence features to predict genes, and among them Prodigal (Hyatt *et al.*, 2010) and MetaGeneMark (Zhu *et al.*, 2010) are the most successful ones. The success of these algorithms can be attributed to the availability of a large number of diverse known genes that offers a better training set, and the improved knowledge of microbial genes that enables a better estimation of gene model parameters.

It is worth noting that gene prediction is still an active research area and several aspects are being improved constantly. For example, the availability of metatranscriptomics data enables accurate prediction of eukaryotic protein-coding genes (Carradec *et al.*, 2018). Taxa-specific models are improving gene prediction accuracy in certain taxa over generic gene models such as viral gene prediction (Zhang *et al.*, 2019), and deep learning methods are being explored to automatically extract sequence features rather than relying on the human expert system to manually select features(Al-Ajlan and El Allali, 2019).

7.1.2 *Discover genes by protein assembly*

For functional diversity and bioprospecting, the proteins encoded by a microbial community may be all what we want. It is also possible to assemble the protein directly without taking the detour of metagenome assembly and gene prediction. Protein assembly could also bypass the complexity faced in de Bruijn graphs caused by strain-level genetic variations and repeats.

There are very few *de novo* protein assemblers. One of them, Plass, is particular interesting (Steinegger *et al.*, 2019b). Plass uses a greedy iterative assembly strategy without constructing a graph. The basic idea of Plass is first identify the overlap between protein fragments (translated from short reads), and then iteratively extend the fragments by "walking" via overlap. The key challenge is identifying overlap among billions of short fragments. Plass avoids all-vs-all comparison by inventing a kmer based approach that scales linearly in runtime and memory. Plass was used to assembly some of the largest datasets such as the TARA ocean metagenome project (Steinegger *et al.*, 2019b).

Like Prodigal, Plass could not reliably predict eukaryotic genes due to the presence of exon-intron structure. For eukaryotic gene discovery, most eukaryotic gene callers require transcriptomics data or an annotated close relative related organism in addition to sequence features to train gene models (Levy Karin *et al.*, 2020). Neither of the two are reliable, however. The sequence features are less conserved among eukaryotic genomes than prokaryotic genomes, and the eukaryotic reference genome databases are much smaller.

7.2 Function Annotation

Most gene prediction programs provide structural information such as the start and end positions of the gene, start and end positions of the CDS (CoDing Sequence) for protein coding genes, and for eukaryotic genes, exon/intron coordinates. Function annotation is a process that computationally assigns putative functions to a predicted gene found in the gene discovery process. In the metagenomics context, protein function annotation is the main focus, although noncoding RNA genes can be annotated using a similar approach. From a metagenomics perspective, the goal of function annotation is to predict the molecular function of a gene's products. As it is assumed that sequence similarity indicates an functional similarity, we can infer a query protein's function based on its sequence homology to known reference proteins (homologs). If a query to its target are orthologs, or they directly share an ancestor instead of related via gene duplication events (paralogs), function inference can be more reliable, as ancestral functions are more likely to be retained between orthologous genes than between paralogs (Tatusov *et al.*, 1997).

From a data engineering perspective, the function annotation process labels a gene with a vector of probabilities, with each probability representing how likely this gene has a known function. The resulting matrix would be very sparse if all results are kept for millions of genes and tens of thousands of known functions. Most of the time, however, only the largest probability is kept for each of the millions of genes predicted from a metagenome dataset to reduce space. As many other computational metagenomics problems, function annotation also faces a data engineering problem: millions of proteins often need to be annotated in a single experiment.

From an algorithmic perspective, the functional annotation problem is analogous to find the nearest neighbor of a new protein and take their labels (known functions). These labels are often derived from Gene Ontology (GO terms, http://geneontology.org/). For example, GO describes the activities of gene products at the molecular level with 11,169 terms as of May 2021. To find the nearest neighbor, either an alignment-based sequence homology search is performed to find the best hit, or a model-based search is performed to assign a protein to known protein families.

7.2.1 *Alignment-based protein annotation*

The enormous amount of sequence in a typical metagenomics overwhelms traditional sequence alignment-based tools such as BLAST. If we could afford to sacrifice sensitivity by limiting the search to highly similar sequences, there are faster algorithms such as BLAT (Kent, 2002) and Usearch (Edgar, 2010). These methods are based on the seed-and-extend paradigm for sequence comparison, in which the exact occurrences of seeds (or kmers) contained in the query can be quickly found in the reference sequences, and these seed matches are then extended via a slower, full alignment process between the queries and potential target references. Shorter seeds increase sensitivity, whereas longer seeds increase speed. BLAT employs longer seeds, whereas Usearch uses multiple short seeds for prioritization, and both achieve 100 times faster than BLAST.

These programs, however, are still not fast enough to query millions of metagenomic sequences against a growing database with tens of billions of genes. By combining the advantages of modern computing architecture and breakthroughs in algorithms, a recent algorithm achieves a speed 20,000 times faster than BLAST with similar sensitivity (Buchfink *et al.*, 2015). Here, I want to highlight a few of the algorithmic tricks that this software, DIAMOND, uses to speed up the homology search.

DIAMOND is also based on seed-and-extend strategy. As many other programs, DIAMOND indexes the seeds from the reference database, which allows the rapid identification of potential matches. With a large reference database, the seed index becomes very big. Since some of the amino acids are similar to each other (as organisms tend to use them interchangeably, such as K and R), they can be grouped together to be treated as one during the similarity search. These "interchangeable" amino acids could be inferred from a large number of BLAST alignments. Originally developed by Dr. Yuzhen Ye's group at Indiana University in its "Reduced Alphabet based Protein similarity Search" (RAPSearch) tool, the reduced alphabet can greatly reduce memory usage and increase search speed (Zhao *et al.*, 2012). Here, instead of using the full 20 amino acids as the alphabet, DIAMOND only uses 11, effectively reducing the size of the seed index.

Besides the reduced alphabet, a second trick that DIAMOND uses is spaced seeds. A spaced seed is essentially a longer seed, but only a subset of its positions are used. A single spaced seed can be faster than a contiguous seed, while retaining sensitivity by adding more subsets of its position to be used.

The unique trick that distinguishes DIAMOND from other programs that are also using reduced alphabets and spaced seeds, is that it also indexes the query sequences. A DIAMOND index is an ordered list of seed-location pairs. By indexing both query and reference sequences, DIAMOND translates the homology search problem into a well-known computer science problem, i.e., database sort-merge joining, as each index is essentially a database.

DIAMOND represents an excellent example of combining innovations in metagenomics (reduced alphabet), data engineering (seed indexing), and many algorithms (spaced seeds, sort-merge joining) to tackle a computational metagenomics problem.

Can the sequence homology search go even faster? Surely it can. The reference database contains a large number of very similar sequences (redundancy), it is not necessary to compare this group of very similar sequences if the query shares no homology with a representative sequence in the group. Martin Steinegger and Johannes Söding developed a tool called Linclust, which clusters the reference sequences into clusters and selects a representative sequence from each cluster. This way, the homology search can be 1600 times faster than DIAMOND (Steinegger and Söding, 2018). The authors similarly took a strategy to derive a reduced representation of each protein sequence (a group of kmers), and leveraged existing sorting algorithms in computer science to cluster similar proteins. Linclust clustered IMG/M 1.59 billion protein sequences into 424 million clusters in 10 hours on a 2×14-core server.

7.2.2 *Model-based protein annotation*

A cluster of similar sequences can be aligned together to derive a sequence model, which is a statistical representation of this group of proteins. Given a multiple sequence alignment, we can either build a Position Specific Scoring Matrix (PSSM) to model the probability of amino acids at each position, or a probabilistic Hidden Markov Model (HMM) that also includes position-specific probabilities for insertions and deletions. Searching query proteins with protein models instead of the sequences themselves increases sensitivity, as models suppress evolutionary noise while elevating true signals.

You may already be familiar with NCBI's PSI-BLAST (Position-Specific Iterative Basic Local Alignment Search Tool), which derives a PSSM from the multiple sequence alignment of sequences returned from a regular Blast search. This PSSM is then used to search the database for new matches and is updated for subsequent iterations with these newly detected sequences. While PSI-BLAST provides a means of detecting distantly related homologs, its computational intensive nature prevents its application in large-scale protein annotation.

Without going into details about how HMM works as it should be explained in most of many basic bioinformatics textbooks, I will focus the remaining of this section on its application in large-scale function annotation. A major benefit of HMM-based annotation is due to the Pfam databases (http://pfam.xfam.org/), the HMMER software suite (http://hmmer.org/, [Eddy (2011)]), and computing resources derived from them. The identification of protein domains via HMM can provide insights into the potential function of a query protein. In the cow rumen metagenome project I was involved in, we identified 27,755 candidate genes with a significant match to at least one relevant catalytic domain or carbohydrate-binding module, suggesting their potential function in carbohydrate metabolism (Figure 7.1, [Hess *et al.* (2011)]).

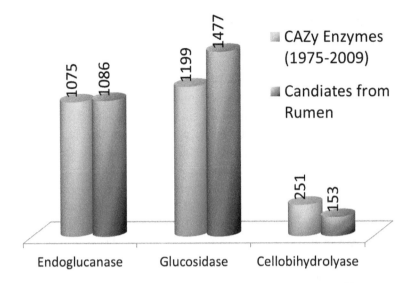

Fig. 7.1 Candidate enzymes discovered from the cow rumen metagenome project.

There are some limitations of HMM-based homology search. First, the protein families annotated in Pfam are not comprehensive. For example, a HMMER search using over a billion nonredundant protein sequences from EMBL-EBI's metagenomics database was able to annotate 58% of the sequences (https://f1000research.com/posters/8-444). The researchers were able to build 699 novel protein families from some large protein clusters with over 1000 sequences. Second, the speed of HMMER is comparable to BLAST, so it would be impractical to use HMMER on a dataset with billions of sequences. Finally, HMMER does not produce orthologs of the queries (neither does DIAMOND), as the best hit of a query is not a guarantee of an ortholog. Annotations derived from paralogs may greatly reduce accuracy because paralogs are more likely to evolve different functions.

While building new curated HMM models may take time, the last two limitations can be partially relieved by new algorithms. For example, the eggNOG-mapper pipeline uses a two-step process by first using DIAMOND to find highly similar homologs, followed by using HMMER for a more sensitive search (Huerta-Cepas *et al.*, 2017). It then applies taxonomic restrictions to ortholog discovery to reduce the search space as well as to increase true positives.

7.2.3 *Detecting distant protein homology*

DIAMOND and tools alike are up to four orders of magnitude faster than BLAST, making it possible to search massive amounts of metagenome sequences, assembled or not, for highly similar matches among the fast-growing databases of reference sequences. Profile HMM-based methods such as HMMER, with a small cost in decreasing speed, further increase the search sensitivity, enabling the annotation of many more protein sequences. However, as we have seen in the above billion-sequence HMMER project, no homology could be found for a large fraction (42%) of the proteins predicted from metagenomes.

DIAMOND and HMMER are useful to detect similarities between sequences that have not diverged beyond "the twilight zone" of sequence similarity (defined as 20%–30% sequence identities). However, the protein structure may stay the same while the underlying sequence changes significantly during evolution. This distant homology is much harder to detect, but could be very useful in the context of metagenomics, and greater diversity often translates into greater divergence.

To prioritize real distant homologs over background noise, two strategies are currently being explored. First, one could add structural-level similarity on top of sequence-level similarity, for example, incorporate secondary structure information to prioritize those homologs with lower sequence similarity. Second, instead of using query sequences directly to search a database of sequences or models, one could construct a HMM model first, and then use the model to search a database of models. By summarizing multiple similar sequences in the query set into a model, the search can be faster and the results can be more sensitive to detect weaker homology. The HH-Suite3 software tool implements both strategies for sensitive search to detect distant homologs (Steinegger *et al.*, 2019a).

7.3 Pathway Analysis

To understand the function of a gene, it is often necessary to put it in its context. Linking multiple genes that perform related reactions such as those in a metabolic pathway and analyzing them as a unit, or pathway analysis, offers a higher level view of the function diversity of a microbial community. Some metabolic pathways are encoded in clusters of physically adjacent genes, known as biosynthetic gene clusters (BGCs). Mining BGCs has the promise to discover novel microbial natural products that have potential biomedical or industrial properties.

Similar to protein function profiling, pathway profiling maps annotated genes to those contained in reference pathway databases and produce both the presence/absence and the abundance of each reference pathway in a metagenome dataset (compositional analysis). Through pathway enrichment analysis, one could track the dynamic changes in the functional diversity of a community.

7.3.1 *Common pathway databases*

7.3.1.1 *Kyoto Encyclopedia of Genes and Genomes (KEGG)*

KEGG is a widely used reference database that contains high-order function annotations (pathways, modules, etc. https://www.genome.jp/kegg/). Its latest release, Release 98.1 on May 1, 2021, contains 781,736 pathways and 545 maps (manually curated knowledge about molecular interactions, reactions, and relations). The database is updated regularly and offers rich APIs as well as web interfaces for pathway analysis. KEGG maps are represented as graphs, where nodes are molecules such as proteins or compounds, and edges represent relation types between the nodes, such as activation or phosphorylation. KEGG organizes maps in an organism-independent manner, i.e., the maps represent our current knowledge of known biochemical reactions, regardless whether or not these reactions are present in the same organism. Therefore, an organism rarely contains the full set of all reactions annotated in a KEGG map. Figure 7.2 shows an example of a KEGG map.

7.3.1.2 *MetaCyc Metabolic Pathway Database*

MetaCyc is a curated database of experimentally elucidated metabolic pathways from all domains of life (https://metacyc.org/). Currently, MetaCyc contains 2,937 pathways from 3,295 different organisms. In contrast to KEGG that organizes pathways according to compounds and biochemical reactions, MetaCyc organizes pathways according to their physiological role in an organism. These pathways are also organism-specific, i.e., there could be multiple representations of a KEGG pathway in different organisms that differ by a few reactions. MetaCyc also

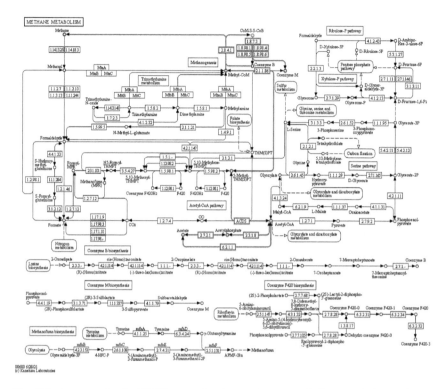

Fig. 7.2   An example of a KEGG map, showing mathane metabolism, with the mathano-genesis between mathane and acetate highlighted in red. Enzyme names or their EC numbers are in boxes, while compounds are in small circles. The map can be explored from this link: https://www.genome.jp/pathway/map00680+C04832

offers options to show all organisms in one pathway, with each organism represented in color. Figure 7.3 shows an example of a MetaCyc pathway.

7.3.2   *Metabolic pathway profiling*

To identify and quantify the metabolic pathways encoded in a community, one could first identify the functions encoded using the algorithms we discussed in the above section, and then map these functions to reference pathways included in databases such as KEGG or MetaCyc. There are two challenges one has to solve, however. First, as we discussed several times already, genes representing important pathway components can fall out of detection due to the low sequencing depth or that they are

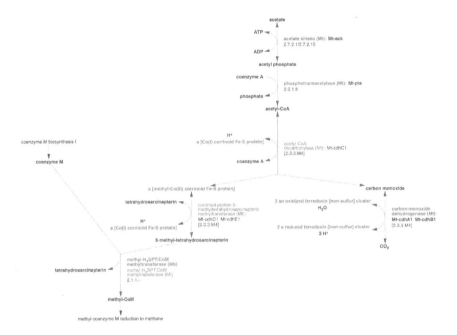

Fig. 7.3 An example of a MetaCyc pathway, showing mathanogenesis between math-ane and acetate. Metabolites are nodes, biochemical reactions are shown on the left of the edges, and enzyme names/EC numbers are shown on the right. Species names are shown in purple color. The map can be explored from this link: https://metacyc.org/META/NEW-IMAGE?type=PATHWAY&object=METH-ACETATE-PWY&&EXP-ONLY=NIL &ENZORG=NIL

too divergent to be identified by the function annotation process (incom-pleteness). Second, the same genes could exist in multiple pathways in different pathways that are difficult to partition (redundancy).

MinPath (Minimal set of Pathways) is a parsimony approach to con-servatively identify metabolic pathways by determining the minimal set of biological pathways that must exist to explain the input protein sequences sampled from a biological system. MinPath addresses both incomplete and redundant challenges (Ye and Doak, 2009).

Built upon the pathways identified by MinPath, HUMAnN (the HMP Unified Metabolic Analysis Network), uses a tiered approach to effi-ciently tackle the incomplete problem: it first maps the reads to marker genes, and then maps the reads to the pangenomes identified by the marker genes. Both of these two steps are efficient as short read align-ment is efficient. After these two steps, a third mapping step, the most inefficient step, is done at the translated protein level to recruit more unmapped reads. Pathway abundance is derived by using several tricks to reconcile the redundancy problem (Franzosa *et al.*, 2018).

7.3.3 *Pathway enrichment analysis*

By the presence or absence of certain pathways, we may infer the metabolic capacity of an organism, or compare those of different organisms. In the metagenomics context, compositional analysis (what pathways are present/absent) is not as useful as comparative analysis that tracks community changes in different conditions or time points. To illustrate this point, let me share a study I was involved in 2014.

The study aimed to account microbial organisms in sheep rumen for methane production, as methane is the second largest contributor to global warming with about a third from livestock as a byproduct (Shi *et al.*, 2014). The main source of methane production is a group of archaea known as methanogens. Previously, people observed that one group of sheep consistently produced more methane than the other from the same breed with the same feed, so gut microbiome must be responsible for the difference, rather than sheep genetics or food. To identify which microbial organisms or metabolic pathways are responsible for this difference, we built a reference metagenome by assembling short-read DNA sequences, as well as generating metatranscriptome sequences from each sample. By mapping the transcriptome reads to KEGG pathways, we were able to compare their activity among different samples and identify what pathways are associated with methane-producing phenotype. We found the methane metabolism pathway was the most significantly enriched pathway among about 300 known KEGG pathways and further identified several novel gene clusters encoding this pathway (Shi *et al.*, 2014).

How does one map an annotated gene to a reference pathway? In the above study, we used Blast to associate a query protein with a KEGG function by assigning it a KEGG Orthology (KO) number, with each number being a manually curated protein family. As we discussed above, Blast is not an efficient way for large metagenomic datasets. HMM-based methods have also been developed for KO number assignment with better accuracy and speed. For example, KofamScan searches against a database of profile hidden Markov models (KOfam) with precomputed adaptive score thresholds (Aramaki *et al.*, 2020). Testing it on a dataset with 20 prokaryote genomes showed that it took only 12 minutes for KofamScan while a Blast alternative took over 16 hours for KO number assignment.

How could one associate a pathway with a particular phenotype? Like gene set enrichment analysis used in transcriptomics, pathway enrichment analysis is a specific type of enrichment analysis that tests whether or not a list of genes in a pathway is enriched in a particular sample. There are several methods developed for pathway enrichment analysis. Most of them are developed in the context of clinical genomics, as there is great interest to study disease-associated genetic pathway changes. Nevertheless, the same methods can be similarly applied in metagenome datasets. A practical guide to perform an enrichment analysis can be found in [Reimand *et al.* (2019)]. When applied any of the methods in metagenomics, one needs to consider two key questions: what kind of statistical tests should be used to maximize power and how false discoveries are controlled.

7.3.4 *Discovering BGCs*

Microbes produce secondary metabolites to increase their survival or compete with other organisms. Unlike the primary metabolites (lipids, amino acids, carbohydrates, and nucleic acids), these small molecules are not necessary for their growth or reproduction, but play key roles in increasing the fitness of the microbial organisms that produce them in diverse, changing environments. Many of these natural products have special therapeutic properties, such as cholesterol-lowering, anti-tumor, or antibiotic activities. Secondary metabolites are produced by enzymes encoded by biosynthetic pathways. The enzymes are often organized in a cluster of genes that are in physical proximity in the genome, and thus named as biosynthetic gene clusters (BGCs). The curated Minimum Information about a BGC (MIBiG) database (version 2.0, https://mibig.secondarymetabolites.org/, [Kautsar *et al.* (2020)]) includes 1,434 manually curated BGCs with known functions. Besides microbes, plants can also produce secondary metabolites, as MIBiG includes 19 derived from plant species. In a recent study, researchers identified 1,159 BGCs from just a few hundreds of genomes from soil samples from a northern Californian grassland (Crits-Christoph *et al.*, 2018). Most of these BGCs lacked any homology to gene clusters from MIBiG, suggesting that known BGCs are a tiny fraction of the total BGC diversity.

Discovering BGCs from assembled metagenomes is a challenging process involving two major steps: gene cluster prediction and secondary metabolite prediction. The software tool, AntiSMASH (Blin *et al.*, 2019), is a central tool for the identification of biosynthetic gene clusters of secondary metabolites. AntiSMASH maintains a profile HMM database built from core genes in known BGCs (signature gene pHMMs) and uses it to identify candidate gene clusters from a input metagenome. Clusters of signature gene pHMM hits spaced within a certain distance are used to define gene clusters. Once the clusters are identified, they are subject to several downstream analysis in parallel, including domain architecture analysis, substrate specificity, stereochemistry, and final structure prediction. The software provides a user-friendly web interface and uses JSON format for ease of API integration with other tools.

7.4 Future Perspectives

The gene-revolved analysis sits in between the taxonomy-revolved we discussed in the last chapter and the genome-revolved analysis we are going to learn in the next chapter. Gene- and pathway-level analysis, especially comparative analysis, not only reveals the functional potential of microbial communities, but also correlates these potentials with the observed phenotype. With more functional omics data, including metatranscriptome, metaproteome, and metabolome, we can validate the functional predictions based on the metagenome. Moreover, recent advances in fluxomics (flux-based modeling of metabolism) have made it possible to model microbial communities (Henry *et al.*, 2016).

Although alignment-based and HMM-based methods remain as the mainstream methods for function annotation, methods that include structural information are emerging. The paucity of solved protein structures and the lack of structure prediction algorithms have hampered their adoption. With the fruits of high-throughput structural genomics initiatives and deep learning-based structure prediction tools like AlphaFold2, in the near future, we may be able to significantly improve the accuracy of function annotation, especially for detecting distant homologs. This possibility was recently demonstrated in a study that discovered several new protein families from the Tara Ocean metagenome dataset using structural prediction (Wang *et al.*, 2019a).

Both sequence-based and structure-based homology to infer protein function belong to a broad category of hypothesis-driven or supervised methods. These methods are not designed to uncover new functions, or "unknown unknowns". Metagenome gene annotation pipelines would label a large fraction of proteins as "hypothetical proteins" as they do not have any closely related homologs that we can learn from. Similarly, BGCs predicted from AntiSMASH are also "known knowns" or "known unknowns". We expect to see the rise of unsupervised or data-driven approaches in the future. The decRiPPter (Data-driven Exploratory Class-independent RiPP TrackER) tool is an example of unsupervised approaches, and it relies on the detection of outlier operons from a pangenome rather an homology (Kloosterman *et al.*, 2020).

Chapter 8

Deconvolute Community Metagenome into Single Genomes

Resolving a community metagenome into individual constituent genomes is a prerequisite for many downstream metagenomics analyses, ranging from assessing an individual genome's metabolic capacity, discovering new branches of the tree of life, to interrogating interspecies interactions. There are both experimental and informatics strategies to deconvolute a metagenome. Experimental strategies include high-throughput, single-organism microculture and single-cell metagenomics. We will further discuss this topic in the next chapter. These experimental approaches are limited by the number of species they can reach and incur high experimental costs. Therefore, the vast majority of projects resolve to informatics strategies such as metagenome assembly and binning. In this chapter, I will focus our discussion on informatics strategies. I will cover quite a few topics, first the challenges associated with metagenome assembly, then the assembly itself, followed by metagenome binning and clustering, two procedures that complement the assembly process. I will discuss how one can evaluate the quality of the assembled genomes. At the end of this chapter, I will discuss new technologies that are being developed to improve metagenome assembly.

8.1 An Overview of Metagenome Assembly

Before the invention of a future sequencing technology that can read an entire chromosome or genome from the beginning to the end, prokaryotic genomes and eukaryotic chromosomes must be broken into smaller pieces for sequencing, resulting in reads, via a whole-genome shotgun (WGS) approach. Assembly is the opposite process: it computationally pieces together these reads into chromosomes or genomes. Therefore, the genome assembly problem is formally defined as the inference of a genome G with length L given one or more sets of reads R derived from G, where R's mean read length $l << L$. Similarly, the metagenome assembly problem is to infer the entire set of genome sequences of a community of microbial species $G1, G2, ...Gn$, given one or more sets of sequence reads R, where the mean read length l is much smaller than the mean genome length L.

Although modern metagenome assemblers have greatly streamlined the process of metagenome assembly, in practice, metagenome assembly still involves quite a few steps and many variations created by including/excluding certain optional steps. A metagenome assembly pipeline generally starts with some preprocessing steps to format and clean the read data, a topic covered in Chapter 5. The reads can be optionally clustered into read clusters, and the clusters are subsequently processed in parallel. In the assembly step, assembly graphs are built from the reads, pruned, and then traversed into larger fragments (contigs) without gaps. In some experiments, long-range mate-pair libraries are used to further connect the contigs into scaffolds, even larger fragments with gaps representing unsequenced genomic regions. Because the assembly and scaffolding steps rarely produce genomes in their entirety, contigs and scaffolds are further grouped to form genome bins in the binning step. Finally, a quality assessment step will select high-quality genome bins as metagenome-assembled genomes (MAGs) for further analysis. This quality evaluation step can either be based on available reference genomes or some generic characteristics. A overview of the process is in Figure 8.1.

8.2 Challenges in Metagenome Assembly

Greek philosopher Aristotle once said, "the whole is greater than the sum of its parts". This also applies to comparing the challenges associated with metagenome assembly to those associated with single genome assembly. The metagenome assembly problem is not only

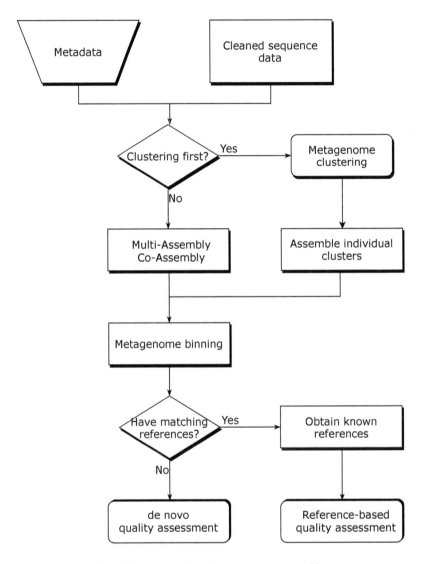

Fig. 8.1   An overview of metagenome assembly.

subject to the general challenges faced in single-genome assembly, but also faces some of its unique ones. To better illustrate these challenges, I will try to explain them in the context of the three aspects of computational metagenomics: metagenomics, data engineering, and algorithm.

8.2.1 *Metagenomics challenges*

The first set of challenges metagenome assembly needs to overcome are the limitations of metagenome sequencing technology and the lack of existing knowledge of most microbial communities. These limitations, combined with the complexity of metagenome datasets, create several unique challenges for metagenome assembly.

8.2.1.1 *Short read length vs repeats*

Initially thought as a unique feature in eukaryotes, repetitive DNA elements (repeats) have been increasingly found in prokaryotes as well. Repeats are sequences that exist in multiple copies in a genome. There are many types of repeats with sizes ranging from a single nucleotide (homopolymer), a short stretch (e.g., transposon), or an entire gene cluster (e.g., ribosomal gene cluster). The number of copies of a repeat in a genome can go from only a few to millions. The similarity among copies of repeats can vary from nearly identical to highly divergent. Their locations can scatter among the genome or organize together at one locus as tandem repeats. Regardless their type or organization in the genome, repetitive regions that are longer than the read length are causing problems for *de novo* assembly. Most genome assemblers give up repetitive regions in the assembly, leaving gaps at where they are located. As a result, genomes assembled from short-read datasets can contain thousands of fragments. In addition to leaving gaps in the assembly, repeats can also cause assemblers to make mistakes during the graph traversal stage, by predicting more copies (repeat expansion) or fewer copies (repeat condensation), or rearranging genome regions (mis-assemblies).

In metagenome assembly, repeats within a genome are similarly causing the above problems. There are also "between-genome repeats" that are unique to metagenomes, including transposons, horizontally transferred genes, and homologous regions that are shared among different genomes. An extreme case of these is that many species can have several highly similar strains within a community. Different strains of the same species share over 97% nucleotide sequence identities, making them difficult or impossible to resolve using short reads. Another special case is the ribosomal RNA genes, which are highly conserved among different species, are also problematic for metagenome assemblers. Despite their usefulness in taxonomy profiling as we discussed in Chapter 6, they are repetitive sequences in the eyes of an assembler.

8.2.1.2 *Limited sequencing depth vs community diversity*

In single-genome assembly projects, we start with a sequencing depth typically at 30-50x, to ensure the majority of the genome can be covered by sequencing. This is because the distribution of the WGS reads follows a Poisson distribution, in the ideal world, an average of 20x read coverage will be required to cover 99% of the regions of a genome at least 10x. As the read coverage is biased instead of being perfectly Poisson (e.g., genomic regions of extreme GC-percentage are poorly sequenced in Illumina sequencing), we would need much higher read depth (typically 30-50x) in practice. The required sequencing for a 3-megabase bacterial isolate genome with 30-50x sequencing depth translates into 0.6 to 1 million 150bp reads (*genome length × sequencing depth ÷ read length*). The larger the genome, the more reads would be required for a good genome coverage and assembly.

If all species in a community have equal abundance, then the required sequencing depth for a metagenome is solely determined by the community richness, or the combined length of all genomes in the community. However, such communities are almost nonexistence in the real world. The species abundance distribution of most communities is very skewed, leading to biased datasets where the majority of the reads are derived from only a few dominant species, while reads from a large number of rare species are hardly seen. We discussed that sequencing depth can limit our ability to study the diversity of a microbial community in Chapter 6 because of the same reason. Similarly, sequencing depth also limits the assembly of rare species. For a metagenome project, it is often not possible to predetermine how many reads we would need for its assembly, as we need to factor in the species abundance distribution to estimate the sequencing effort.

For readers in computer science or other non-biology disciplines, the following analogy may help understand the above concept. As a genome is analogous to a book, a metagenome is analogous to a library of books. Metagenome richness roughly translates to the number of species in a community, or the number of different books in a library. In a catastrophic event, our library of books, thousands of different books, and millions of volumes, all get shredded into smaller pieces. This happens in every metagenome sequencing experiment. The length of the book varies from several thousands to tens of millions of letters. Depending on the sequencing technologies we use, some pieces are short, about 100 letters long, and some are long, several thousands or tens of thousands of letters. Sequencing is all about sampling enough of these pieces so that we may recover most of the books, including those rare ones with only a few copies. Intuitively, we will need to sequence a lot of small pieces for thicker books, and much more if the library has many different books with some rare editions.

8.2.1.3 *Lack of reference genomes for assembly quality assessment*

Being able to directly sequence all microbes without lab cultivation brings an exciting opportunity to fully comprehend the vast diversity of the microbial world and discover novel microbial species we have not seen previously. As much as we want to study environmental habitats that are full of new species, we would have little idea about the quality of the assembly after we assemble them because we do not have similar species to reference to. Since the first dawn of computational metagenomics to today, researchers have been struggling with this challenge. Now they can assemble many genomes in a single experiment, but how do they assess the quality of those completely novel ones? How do they know the genome is complete when they do not know what to expect? How do they identify contaminants if the target and contaminant are both novel? These questions have led to many new creative solutions, and I hope to cover some of them in this chapter.

8.2.2 *Data engineering challenges*

There are two main data engineering obstacles in front of a good metagenome assembly. First, the scale of the input data. For communities with high richness and more skewed species abundance distribution, we need more sequencing depth as we discussed above, but this inevitably produces a larger volume of data. The first MetaHIT

(METAgenomics of the Human Intestinal Tract) project produced 500 Gb (Li *et al.*, 2014), and DOE JGI's cow rumen project produced 1.2 Tb (Hess *et al.*, 2011). The biggest project to date, the Tara Oceans Project, a world-wide ocean survey project, has already produced over 8 Tb (Sunagawa *et al.*, 2020). The title may not hold very long, as the ocean microbial community is not the most complex one. Based on what we have learned about these projects, to get a fair coverage of the microbes in the forest soil, we would need to sequence at least 200 Tb. Remember, we discussed in Chapter 4 that unstructured metagenome data may explode 200 times during analysis!

The other obstacle is the complexity of the assembly process itself. A typical assembly pipeline contains three major steps, each step involves running multiple software tools. We need to clean up the data through a preprocess step, as we discussed in Chapter 5, remove contaminants and sequencing errors. We then need to construct a graph that contains all kmers using some graph data structures to represent the data, which we introduced in Chapter 3 but we will discuss in some detail in the following section. And finally, we would traverse the graph or find a path among kmers to recover the genomes. Each step may have very different requirements for computing resources. The preprocess step is in general IO-intensive, as we are moving large amounts of data across the network, reading/writing them from/to file storage systems, and load/unload them from the memory. The graph construction and graph traversal steps are both memory- and computing-intensive, as the kmer graph may contain billions of nodes and trillions of edges, and parallel processing is required for efficient constructing and traversal. While combining these steps in a single software pipeline greatly reduces the effort to run a metagenome assembly, sometimes it is not an efficient way for utilizing computing resources. We would have to provision the system with a large enough amount of memory to satisfy the most memory-demanding step in the pipeline, and at the same time a large number of CPU cores to meet the need of the most computing-demanding step. This leads to underutilization of the computing resources if most of the time the cores are sitting idle or the memory is largely not occupied. Finally, metagenome assemblers often run a substantially longer time on large datasets, inevitably increasing the risk of hardware/software failures.

8.2.3 *Algorithmic challenges*

As we discussed in Chapter 3, we can translate the genome assembly problem into a graph problem in computer science and solve it. In this case, reads can be treated as strings of an unknown superstring (genome), and the genome assembly problem is very similar to the shortest superstring problem (SSP) in computer science. Unfortunately, the SSP is a NP-hard problem, as it takes exponential time for a solution that always finds the shortest superstring. This means given billions of short reads, we are out of luck, as we may never be able to find the optimal assembly in our lifetime. For a detailed description of this problem and related problems, readers are encouraged to read more about Traveling Salesman, Hamiltonian Paths, NP-hardness, and NP-completeness (Chapters 34 and 35 of "Introduction to Algorithms" by Cormen, Leiserson, Rivest and Stein (Cormen *et al.*, 2009)).

The SSP problem is probably an oversimplified version of the genome assembly problem, for the reasons we discussed above in the metagenomics aspect (Nagarajan and Pop, 2009).

8.3 Metagenome Assembly

Before we discuss metagenome assembly, let us briefly review single-genome assembly process. There are two general strategies for single-genome assembly: reference-based and *de novo* strategy. In reference-based assembly, we choose a reference genome from the same species or a closely related one as a blueprint to guide the assembly process. We use reference-based assembly to discover variations in the new genome by comparing to the reference genome. In *de novo* assembly, we reconstruct the genome directly, without the aid of reference genomes. We can use *de novo* assembly to discover genomes from novel species that are not similar to those we know. In metagenome assembly, we seldom have known references to perform reference-based assembly, therefore I will limit our discussion to *de novo* assembly only.

Most genome assemblers are based on graph algorithms, and predominantly on a single type of graph: the de Bruijn graph. Let us briefly review several key points about this graph structure we introduced in Chapter 3. First, we can represent a genome using a de

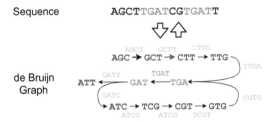

Fig. 8.2 A illustration of a de Bruijn Graph. Pink color represents repeats.

Bruijn graph of kmers, where edges of the graph are kmers and nodes are the shared part between two adjacent edges (k-1 mer) as illustrated in Figure 8.2. In this representation, the genome is a path, or a walk, that visits all edges of this graph at least once. Second, we can construct the de Bruijn graph from sequence reads, and traverse (walk) graph to recover the genome. This is an oversimplified view of genome assembly. Metagenome assembly follows a similar paradigm like single-genome assembly. The presence of sequencing errors and repetitive elements that we mentioned above will add tips and loops to a de Bruijn graph, which makes graph traversal difficult. In practice, metagenome assembly is a much more complicated process, as you will get some ideas from the following discussion.

8.3.1 *Metagenome de Bruijn graph construction*

In de Bruijn-based single-genome assembly, the most influential parameter is the size of kmer (k). We face a dilemma when choosing an optimal k. On the one hand, a bigger k reduces the complexity caused by repeats and simplifies the graph structure. In the graph we showed in Figure 8.2 the loop structure will be gone if we increase k to 5 from 4. However, the longer the k, the higher the chance that a kmer will contain errors, and erroneous kmers lead to dead ends during the graph traversal and fragmented assembly. This problem is more pronounced in genomes sequenced at low coverage. On the other hand, shorter kmers increase the percentage of correct kmers, but inevitably lead to a more complex graph structure that are more prone to traversal errors. Thus, the choice of k is a trade-off between contiguity and correctness. Many modern single-genome assemblers can try assembling the data under several k and pick the best among them. In metagenome assembly, however, there may not be one k that fits all genomes, as different genomes can have very different k parameters for their optimal assembly.

Inspired by the transcriptome assembly problem, where a multi-k approach is adopted to tackle that different transcripts have very different sequencing coverage, some metagenome assemblers, such as metaHipmer, similarly use a multi-k approach. Instead of using a fixed k to construct the de Bruijn graph, metaHipmer first uses a small kmer for the initial graph, then iteratively increases the kmer size in subsequent graphs (Hofmeyr *et al.*, 2020).

8.3.2 *Metagenome de Bruijn graph simplification*

After the de Bruijn graph is constructed in a single-genome assembly project, the graph is then subjected to a graph simplification process to merge unique paths, remove tips caused by erroneous kmers, and resolve small bubbles caused by repeats. Even though the base correction step in the preprocess step (discussed in Chapter 5) can remove the majority of sequencing errors, some remaining errors can lead to tips, sometimes even alternative paths on the graph. Because of the low error rate in short-read sequences, kmers at these tips or paths have a much lower abundance than the main path (below the coverage cutoff threshold), and they can be safely removed.

In metagenome assembly, the graph simplification process may have an unintended consequence. If there is a dominant species and a closely related species with low abundance, kmers from the low abundance species could be accidentally removed because they may appear as "errors".

Even after extensive graph simplification, the resulting assembly graph could still have a complex structure. A nice visualization of an real example is in Figure 8.3 (Wick *et al.*, 2015).

8.3.3 *Parallel graph construction and traversal*

Compared with single-genome assembly, metagenome assembly involves working with a much larger set of kmers, and it is often not possible to hold all kmers in the memory of a single computing node.

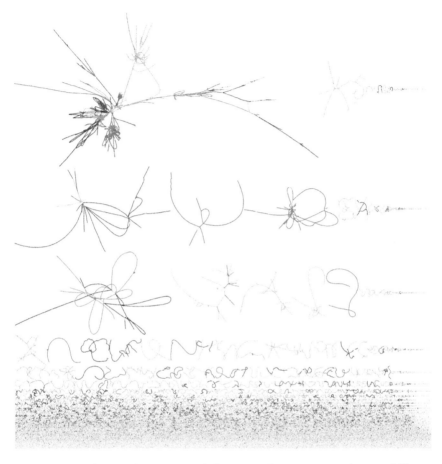

Fig. 8.3 Assembly graphs constructed from a real metagenome dataset. Different genome bins are indicated by different colors. Image source: https://tylerbarnum.com/2018/02/26/how-to-use-assembly-graphs-with-metagenomic-datasets/

Distributed assemblers such as metaHipmer uses a global kmer hash table that is distributed to many nodes, each with a subset of kmers but can be addressed by all nodes. To speed up graph traversal, metaHipmer intelligently allocates kmers belonging to the same region of the graph to the same computing node to reduce the computing cost associated with kmer lookup (Hofmeyr *et al.*, 2020).

Table 8.1 lists the differences between single-genome and metagenome assembly.

Table 8.1 Differences between single-genome assembly and metagenome assembly

	Single Genome	**Metagenome**
Assembly strategies	Reference-based, de novo	de novo
kmer size	single	multiple
coverage cutoff	yes	maybe

8.3.4 *Long reads and other types of graphs*

Long reads derived from PacBio or Oxford Nanopore sequencing technologies gradually entered the metagenome sequencing space. The high error rate in the raw reads makes them not suitable for de Bruijn graph-based assemblers without error correction, as the majority of the kmers contain errors. However, they can be used in a different type of graph – the overlap graph (Myers, 1995), which is constructed by using the reads as nodes and their overlap as edges. To construct such a graph, we would first compute the pairwise read alignments to derive their overlaps (edges). This is a computationally expensive step, as we will have to compute $n(n-1)/2$ number of read pairs (n is the total number of reads) for their overlap. To traverse this graph, we will derive the shortest path so that the nodes are visited at least once. For the overlapping regions, we can derive a consensus to remove sequencing errors. This algorithm is called OLC (overlapping layout consensus), as illustrated in Figure 8.4.

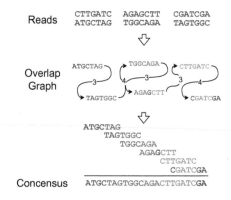

Fig. 8.4   A illustration of the Overlap Layout Consensus algorithm (OLC).

OLC assembly algorithm actually predates the de Bruijn graph. It was the core algorithm used in the Human Genome Project (HGP). The underlying data for the HGP was generated by the Sanger sequencing technology, now referred as first generation sequencing, which contains reads of 500–1000 bases in length and less than 0.1% errors. The development of next-generation sequencing (NGS) exacerbated the challenges faced by the OLC approach. First, NGS reads are much shorter but are many more, which makes pairwise overlap detection computationally intractable as it grows quadratically with the number of nodes. Second, it is more difficult to distinguish a short but real overlap between two reads from that caused by random chance, as NGS reads have a much higher error rate (2%).

Long-read sequencing has since revived OLC in genome assembly, at least for small genomes. For metagenome assembly, long reads can be used in the de Bruijn graph simplification stage, as small repeats can be resolved by them. The long-read assembler CANU (Koren *et al.*, 2017) uses a MinHash-based algorithm for rapid overlap detection and a sparse graph, making it possible for assemble large genomes, even metagenomes, using long noisy reads. Another long-read assembler, metaFlye, uses a creative repeat graph to better resolve repeats using long reads (Kolmogorov *et al.*, 2020).

8.3.5 *Coassembly vs multiassembly*

Metagenome assembly projects, especially those longitudinal studies that track community changes over time or comparative studies across habitats, are increasingly depending on a large number of samples. For such multisample datasets, we could choose two alternative strategies to assemble them: assembly each sample individually and then combine the assemblies (multiassembly), or combine the sequence data and assembly them together (coassembly). Each strategy has its own pros and cons. Coassembly can benefit rare species that are present in multiple samples, as pooling samples increases their sequencing depth. This allows a more robust assembly of these genomes and leads to more assembled genomes with greater completeness. The drawback of coassembly, compared to multiassembly, is that it increases the challenges faced in the metagenome assembly: 1) coassembly has to deal

with a much larger dataset (data engineering challenge); 2) coassembly
has to deal with a much more richer dataset, as species from different
samples are mixed. Strains of the same species are brought together
as well, increasing the complexity of de Bruijn graph traversal (metagenomics and algorithmic challenge). Multiassembly is less challenging
during the assembly stage, but it has to merge different assemblies
together and remove duplicated sequences. Merging assembly has its
own algorithmic challenges. In addition, multiassembly may miss rare
species. In practice, most metagenomes are assembled via the multiassembly strategy, as many metagenome assemblers can only work on
a single computing node, and data from a single sample can easily take
over the entire available computing memory.

   With the advent of distributed metagenome assemblers such
as metaHipmer that makes it possible to assembly large datasets,
coassembly was applied to a complex, large (822 GB) Tara Ocean
metagenome dataset and its results were compared to those from multiassembly (Hofmeyr *et al.*, 2020). Coassembly was found to be able to
assemble both high and low-abundance genomes, and with fewer duplicated sequences.

8.4 Metagenome Binning

The metagenome assembly process we discussed above transforms
short reads into much larger contigs or scaffolds. Due to the various
challenges during the assembly process, most of these contigs are still
small, from a few kilobase (kb) to a few hundred kb, much smaller than
most microbial genomes (megabase range). Metagenome binning, or
binning, is a process to predict a set of bins given a set of contigs from
the metagenome assembly step, such that the contigs within each bin
are likely originated from the same genome. Unlike scaffolding that
determines the relative order of the contigs on a chromosome, binning
determines the genome membership of the assembled contigs or scaffolds. Within each bin, the order of the contigs in the genome is not
determined.

   From an algorithmic perspective, the binning problem could be
treated as either a classification or a clustering problem. The former,
or supervised binning, involves the prediction of the taxonomy of each

contig, then bin contigs according to the predicted taxon. Because our knowledge of microbial diversity is limited, supervised binning does not work well in practice, especially in communities with a large fraction of unknown members. In the following, we will focus on the latter, or unsupervised binning, which bins contigs based on the intrinsic characteristics of the data rather than relying on any known reference genome. There are two main types of data characteristics unsupervised binning relies on: sequence composition and contig abundance. Most of the metagenome binning tools are based on one or both of these characteristics.

8.4.1 *Sequence composition*

As we discussed in Chapter 3, a genomic sequence can be represented as a bag of kmers. Studies have shown that kmer frequency profile, or composition, is a unique signature of a prokaryotic genome, and it can be used to discriminate different species. This signature is also genome-wide, which means that fragments of the same genome display a similar kmer frequency profile. Multiple studies suggest that the tetra-mer nucleotide frequency (TNF, $k = 4$) has the greatest discriminative power (Karlin and Mrázek, 1997; Abe *et al.*, 2003; Dick *et al.*, 2009).

There are $4^4 = 256$ possible tetra-mers. Because some kmers are so-called "canonical" kmers, there are only 138 distinct "canonical" tetra-mers. For example, "AATT" is identical to the reverse complement of "TTAA", both are counted as "AATT", the lexicographically smaller of the two. As a result, each contig is transformed into a frequency vector of 138 in length. Now we can formulate the metagenome binning problem into a mathematical one, i.e., "what contigs belong to the same species?" becomes "what vectors are close to each other in the same 138-dimensional space?". After this translation, we could apply the algorithms developed for clustering vectors to cluster metagenome contigs.

While being computationally efficient to compute and generically applicable to both prokaryotic and eukaryotic genomes, TNF has two major limitations. First, TNF signals get more noisy when the contig size is small, and most metagenome binning tools will give up on contigs smaller than 1kb. Second, TNF does not distinguish closely related species or strains from the same species. Therefore, TNF is seldomly used by itself, and it is almost always combined with other metrics for binning.

8.4.2 *Contig abundance*

Another metric that is generically applicable to all datasets is contig abundance. Defined as the read coverage of the contig, it is computationally efficient to calculate from the mapped reads. The observed abundance of contigs from the same genome is expected to reflect the abundance of the genome in a sample, so two contigs with a large difference in abundance are less likely coming from the same genome. This metric does not have much statistical power until we have many samples from the same community, as the abundance of contigs from the same genome is expected to highly correlate with each other across samples. The more samples we have, the better this metric becomes. Like TNF, we can represent the contig abundance as a vector whose length is the total number of samples, and apply vector-based clustering algorithms.

Unlike TNF, the contig abundance metric has the potential to discriminate different strains of the same species, if they have different abundance across samples. However, this metric becomes unreliable when the number of samples are small, or species that are present at low abundance or show little variation in abundance across samples.

Combining the TNF metric and the contig abundance metric across multiple samples has enabled a few metagenome binning tools to automatically perform metagneome binning in a scalable fashion. In the MetaBAT tool developed by my research group at JGI, we applied Bayesian statistics to calculate probabilistic distances between pairs of contigs based on TNF and contig abundance, and used a graph-based algorithm for metagenome binning (Kang *et al.*, 2019).

8.4.3 *Ensemble binning*

In machine learning, it is a common practice to ensemble several predictive models to obtain better predictive performance than any of the models by itself. This practice is called "ensemble learning". Here, we could similarly apply an "ensemble binning" algorithm, by combining the results from several different metagenome binning tools. Ensemble binning method can achieve better binning results than any individual binning method (Sieber *et al.*, 2018). By doing so, however, one could significantly increase the computing effort as more tools need to be run. Furthermore, it may become difficult to optimize the binning process, as the parameter space to search exponentially increases as more tools are added.

8.5 Metagenome Clustering

I hope by now I have convinced you that metagenome assembly is a very difficult problem. Computer scientists often use a "divide-and-conquer" strategy for approaching difficult problems. By dividing a big problem into two or more smaller problems, and sometimes solving one may greatly expedite another. Could we divide the metagenome assembly problem and conquer it?

The answer is yes. We could group the reads from the same organism together, or apply metagenome clustering, and transform the metagenome assembly problem into assembling many individual genomes. Once reads are clustered, there are already many good solutions for single genome assembly that could be applied to the clusters. This process is also called read binning. This strategy has two immediate benefits. First, each individual read cluster can be assembled in parallel. Second, we could optimize individual genome assembly using their own parameters. The read clustering algorithm is also much simpler to implement. We first determine whether or not two reads overlap. If they do, then it is likely they are derived from adjacent positions of the same genome. We can use the number of k-mers two sequences share to estimate their overlap. Second, we build a read graph with reads as nodes and their overlaps as edges. We then partition the graph into read clusters using a graph partitioning algorithm, such as the label propagation algorithm (Shi *et al.*, 2018).

Although read clustering is much easier than metagenome assembly to implement, it still faces many challenges faced by metagenome assembly: repetitive elements, complex community structure, and large data sizes. It requires higher read coverage for effective clustering of short reads, as a single gap in sequencing coverage will break reads from the same genome into two clusters. Read clusters, however, offer much more robust statistics than single reads, and they could be further merged by sequence composition or abundance covariance similarly as in metagenome binning.

8.6 Genome Quality Assessment

By combining affordable high-throughput sequencing, modern data engineering, and new algorithms, the number of genomes assembled from metagenome datasets (metagenome-assembled genomes, or MAGs) is growing exponentially. It is now possible to identify over 100,000 MAGs in a single study (Pasolli *et al.*, 2019). However, there are increasing concerns regarding the quality of these MAGs. Are they complete, or do they contain all genetic information in this organism? Are they free of contamination from other species? To quantitatively measure the quality of MAG of bacteria and archaea, a set of criteria, the minimum information about a MAG (MIMAG) standard, was specified in 2017 by a group researchers (Bowers *et al.*, 2017).

MIMAG classifies MAGs into four categories: finished, high, medium, and low-quality (Table 8.2). Here, the completeness of a MAG is defined as the percent of observed single-copy marker genes of the total expected single-copy marker genes. Contamination is the percentage of unexpected single-copy marker genes, or single-copy maker genes that appear more than once. The single-copy marker genes refer to a core set of universally conserved genes that are present in almost all species across the three domains of life. The set of core genes that have not gone through gene duplication, the single-copy core genes, can serve as marker genes to estimate the completeness and contamination in the MAGs. Almost all of these genes are involved in the protein translation machinery and are likely to play essential roles in the survival of the species(Harris *et al.*, 2003). To increase the resolution of such estimation, domain-specific, or even clade-specific marker genes can be used. For instance, CheckM tool (Parks *et al.*, 2015), defines single-copy marker genes as those present in at least 97% of genomes in a domain (bacteria: 104 markers; archaea: 150 markers).

MIMAG, as its name suggests, only provides a minimum set of standards to report MAG quality. Some assembly quality evaluation tools, such as MetaQuast, report much more information (Mikheenko *et al.*, 2016). These include assembly statistics (N50, L50, largest contig,

Table 8.2 MIMAG classifies MGAs into four categories: finished, high, medium, and low-quality.

MAG Quality	Finished	High	Medium	Low
Completeness	100%	> 90%	>= 50%	< 50%
Contamination	0%	< 5%	< 10%	< 10%
Description	Single contiguous sequence without gaps or ambiguities with a consensus error rate <= 0.01%	Multiple fragments where gaps span repetitive regions. Presence of the 23S, 16S, and 5S rRNA genes and at least 18 tRNAs.	Many fragments with little to no review of assembly other than reporting of standard assembly statistics.	Many fragments with little to no review of assembly other than reporting of standard assembly statistics.

number of contigs, assembly size, percentage of reads that map back to the assembly, and number of predicted genes per genome, etc). These tools can be more useful with some known references. In that case, they can not only report more accurate metrics such as genome recovery rate, but can also report misassemblies.

8.7 Metagenome Assembly in the Context of Rapid Evolving Technology: Longer Reads, Longer Range

The large gap between metagenome reads and high-quality MAGs is shrinking, thanks to research efforts coming from sequencing technology, high-performance computing, and new algorithms. Two areas are particular interesting: reads are getting longer, and long range information are becoming available.

8.7.1 *Longer reads*

Longer reads reduces the computation requirement, improves gene cluster discovery, and improves assembly quality. By applying longer reads to simplify the assembly graph, we can increase the portion of unique paths in the graph by smoothing more bubbles and resolving more forks. Long reads can be obtained either synthetically or experimentally. Their length can go from a few kbs to hundreds of kbs.

8.7.1.1 *Synthetic long reads*

Several metagenome library preparation techniques enable sequencing large DNA fragments in parallel. Short reads derived from each fragment are assembled into a long read. To be distinguished from the true long-read sequencing that we will discuss below, this type of sequencing is called "synthetic long-read sequencing". For example, Illumina synthetic long-read technology begins by fragmenting genomic DNA to approximately 10 kilobases, each fragment is then amplified and marked with a unique barcode. The short reads resulted from subsequent sequencing are then separated based on their barcodes and assembled into synthetic long reads.

8.7.1.2 *Single-molecule, long read sequencing*

Low throughput and high error rates associated with earlier generations of single-molecule, long-read sequencing have prevented their wide adoption in metagenome sequencing. In recent years, the sequencing cost of PacBio or ONT sequencing is getting closer to that of Illumina. ONT Prometheon sequencing can generate several Tbs sequences in a single run, making it applicable to complex microbial communities. Algorithms employing self-error correction, combined with sequencing the same molecule multiple times to derive a consensus, have greatly reduced the error rate in long reads to a level rivaling Illumina. In a recent study, Singleton et al. sequenced over 1 Tb from microbial communities from a Danish wastewater treatment plant using ONT sequencing and recovered over 1,000 high-quality MAGs, including many circular genomes (Singleton *et al.*, 2020). These circular genomes, representing microbial complete genomes end to end, include full-length rRNA genes that are often missed in MAGs assembled from short-read datasets. This achievement is made possible by new scalable long-read assemblers such as CANU (Koren *et al.*, 2017) and metaFlye (Kolmogorov *et al.*, 2020).

8.7.2 **Longer range**

In metagenome sequencing, we often employ pair-end "jumping libraries". A jumping library is a library of large genomic fragments, normally several kbs in length, that are sequenced from both ends.

They provide longer ranges, which is useful to resolve alternative paths in the assembly graph. The maximum size these libraries can go is limited by molecular biology to about 200 kb, a size enough to resolve genes or even gene clusters, but not strains. Is it possible to get even longer ranges?

Genomic DNA within a cell, be it a prokaryotic or an eukaryotic one, forms complex 3D structures by DNA binding proteins. These structures bring loci that are distant along the chromosome or between different chromosomes in physical proximity. These long-range genetic interactions could be harnessed to facilitate metagenome assembly and binning. One of such techniques is Hi-C. It starts from chemically cross-linking of cells to fix the DNA/protein complexes, followed by digestion with restriction enzymes and ligation of the interacting loci. These loci are then detected by high-throughput whole-genome shotgun sequencing. Figure 8.5 provides a schematic view of a typical Hi-C experiment to reveal two interacting loci. As Hi-C can catalog genome-wide long-range interactions, it should facilitate metagenome binning.

8.8 Future Perspectives: A Roadmap for a Finished Metagenome Assembly

Currently, very few genomes assembled from metagenomes have "finished" quality, i.e., with 100% of the genes in a single ungapped sequence and without any contamination (according to MIMAG standards). There is no formal definition of a finished metagenome yet. Here let us tentatively define it as 99.99% of the genomes in the community have been assembled with a "finished" status. While achieving this is not required for most metagenomics studies and currently we are far from that for any complex community, it is nevertheless a fun exercise to imagine a potential road map that might lead us to a finished metagenome assembly in the future.

In the near future, sequencing reads are getting longer and more accurate. Eventually, the read length will reach or exceed the current upper limit of high molecular weight DNA libraries, around 200 kb. As they are much bigger than the repetitive sequences, the size of the assembly graph will be greatly reduced and its traversal becomes much easier. Misassemblies will be rare. Many small genomes, such

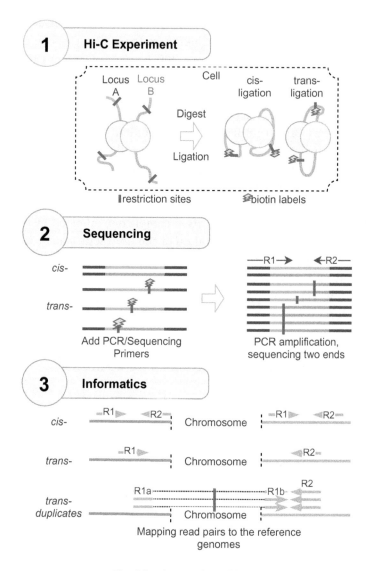

Fig. 8.5   An overview of Hi-C.

as viruses and plasmids, do not need assembly at all. Highly similar strains, even those with 99% identities, will be reliably resolved. Highly conserved gene clusters such as ribosomal gene clusters and tRNA gene clusters, will not be missed any more.

In the near future, the assemblers will be much more efficient and smarter. With longer reads, building and traversing assembly graphs will happen in minutes, not in hours and days, even for large metagenome projects. With increasingly more genomes available in the reference database, the assemblers will leverage known information as an assembly guide for faster and more accurate assembly. The future smarter assemblers will take an iterative approach to optimize assembly. It will automatically build machine learning models based on the initial assembly, and then iteratively improve the assembly of each genome by recruiting new reads in each iteration. It will automatically fill small gaps under the guidance of a well-trained, deep generative neural network. For that, a JGI researcher, Robert Riley, kindly wrote a poem to help us imagine the future metagenome assembler:

> *Though now less a science, than art*
> *Metagenome assemblers, if smart*
> *Will use new information*
> *At each iteration*
> *With AI, build the whole from its parts*

Chapter 9

Single Cell Metagenomics

In previous chapters, we discussed computational approaches to dissect the complexity of metagenomics. To get a high-level, low-resolution view of a community and answer taxonomic diversity questions such as "who is there?", we use targeted analysis of marker genes such as the 16S rRNA gene. To understand the functional diversity, we would turn to gene discovery and pathway prediction using whole metagenome shotgun sequencing (WGS) that sequences the community as a whole. To gain a higher resolution at the single species level, we employ metagenome assembly and binning to reduce a microbial community into individual species.

In parallel with the rapid development of informatics approaches, experimental methods have also made great strides in reducing the complexity of metagenomics. Various strategies have been developed that can effectively decrease the richness of a community. For example, partitioning a community into subcommunities by separating microbial cells based on their physical properties such as size, DNA content, or the presence/absence of certain markers. Subcommunities of interest can also be selected based on the metabolic properties of their members, such as using "enrichment culture" techniques to select a subset of microbes that can grow in a particular predefined culture condition. While these partitioning strategies can make the computational metagenomics problem more manageable, they face similar data and algorithmic challenges in metagenome assembly and functional annotation. They are not able to reliably distinguish organisms at the subspecies level or at the individual cell level. Taking this partitioning strategy to an extreme, it is possible to use high-throughput technologies to culture and sequence single cells in parallel. A total of 7,781 genomes were obtained this way in a recent study of the human gut microbiome(Groussin *et al.*, 2021). These genomes span 339 species, and 13% of them were missed by previous studies with the WGS approach. With genomes derived from single clones, the authors were able to draw the conclusion that human gut bacteria continuously acquire new functionality via horizontal gene transfer (HGT), and the rate of HGT is linked to the host's lifestyle.

With technologies such as Fluorescence Activated Cell Sorting (FACS) and droplet microfluidics, a community can now be partitioned into individual cells. Advances in sequencing also enabled sequencing the genome from a single cell without culture, so began the era of single-cell genomics era. In this chapter, we will discuss single-cell metagenomics, or using single-cell genomic sequencing to study a microbial community, one cell at a time. Here, I would like to draw the distinction between metagenomics based on single-cell genome sequencing and metagenomics based on high-throughput isolate genome sequencing (single-colony sequencing) mentioned above. In both approaches, single cells can be isolated from environmental samples using serial dilution, microfluidics, FACS, or micromanipulation, and subsequently processed in a high-throughput manner. In single cell genome sequencing, single cells are directly sequenced without culture, therefore the original state of their genomes (DNA sequence, modification, etc) is preserved. In contrast, single-colony sequencing involves culturing and sequencing single cells in parallel via lab automation technologies. By combining droplet microfluidics and high-throughput DNA sequencing, single-colony sequencing can also analyze millions of distinct microbial cells (Villa *et al.*, 2019). This is an exciting new development and it may combine the best of two worlds: isolate genomics and metagenomics. This "colony-in-parallel" approach is very powerful and can be applied to communities with low species richness, however, it may miss species that are not amendable to lab culture. In the following sections, I will focus on the computational aspects of single cell metagenomics, although they could be applied to single-colony metagenomics as well.

9.1 Single-cell Amplified Genome (SAG)

With a full set of genetic instructions (genome) and a full set of bio-chemical machinery, a single cell is the fundamental unit of life. They can form highly specialized cell types in multicellular eukaryotic organisms, but in bacteria, archaea, and protists, an individual cell is a complete organism. The need to fully understand genetic and metabolic variations within a species, as well as their interactions, drives the rapid development of single cell omics, including genomics, transcriptomics, proteomics, and metablomics, all at the single cell level (Wang and Bodovitz, 2010). Here I will focus our discussion on single cell genomics in the context of metagenomics.

Unlike a high eukaryotic cell that has a large genome with two or more copies, most bacterial cells have a single-copy, small-sized genome. For comparison, a human cell contains two copies of a 3 Gbp genome, about 6 picogram of DNA (a picogram is one trillionth of a gram or 10^{-12} g). In contrast, a bacterial cell with a single copy 3 Mbp genome contains only ~3 femtograms (or 3×10^{-15} g). For reference, we often need nanograms (10^{-9} g) or even micrograms (10^{-6} g) of DNA to construct a sequencing library, which translates into millions to trillions of bacterial cells! Therefore, an effective method to amplify genomic DNA from a single cell millions of times is a prerequisite for single cell sequencing. The most common amplification method is multiple displacement amplification (MDA, [Dean *et al.* (2002)]). MDA employs a high-fidelity DNA polymerase derived from a bacterial phage, Phi29, to amplify genomic DNA released from the lysis of a single cell. MDA can yield tens of micrograms of DNA from a single bacterial cell, equivalent to billions of copies of its genome. With MDA, it is now possible to assemble a single cell bacterial genome, and the genomes obtained this way are called Single-cell Amplified Genomes (SAGs).

A typical single cell metagenomics workflow is illustrated in Figure 9.1 (Xu and Zhao, 2018). After single cells are isolated, they are lysed to release their DNA content for MDA-based amplification. The amplified DNA is then undergoing sequencing library construction. During the library construction, DNA from many single cells are pooled together after a unique barcode is added to each cell. The library is

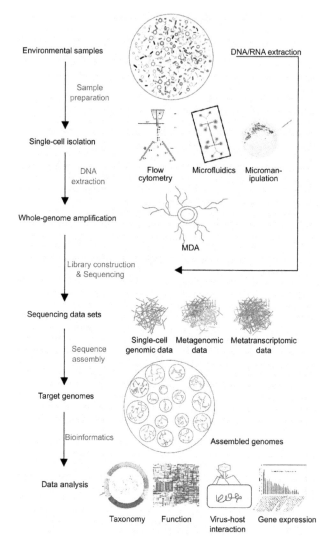

Fig. 9.1 Single cell metagenomics workflow. Reproduced "Single-cell metagenomics: challenges and applications"(Xu and Zhao, 2018) with CC-BY 4.0 licence.

then sequenced by next-generation sequencing. Like the metagenomic sequence data, the single-cell sequence data are processed before they can be used to study taxonomy- and function diversity, gene and species discovery, etc.

9.2 Unique Challenges and Solutions Associated with SAG Assembly

The power of MDA brings the possibility of SAG, but at the meantime it also brings some unique challenges. First, because MDA amplifies DNA billions of times, even a tiny DNA contamination will also get amplified by a significant amount, and it sometimes overwhelms the target genome. Second, MDA amplification is highly uneven: some regions of the genome can have thousands of copies while some can be completely missed. This violates the assumption in single-genome assembly tools that the genome coverage follows a Poisson distribution. Finally, the highly branched DNA synthesis procedure in MDA can produce DNA rearrangements and thus changes the original genome (Zhang *et al.*, 2006). Below I will discuss solutions to combat these challenges.

9.2.1 *Contamination*

Besides the common types of contamination associated with metagenomics experiments such as sequencing adapters and host DNA we have discussed in Chapter 5, sequence data from single cell metagenomics are often contaminated by data from unexpected sources. For example, a minuscule amount of bacterial DNA is often present in lab reagents, either from engineered bacteria strains that produce enzymes, or from the skin micorbiome of lab workers. Because MDA amplifies DNA millions of times, these types of contamination become visible and sometimes may become dominant. Removing these types of contamination is relatively easy, as they would appear in almost every single cell library of the same batch of experiments. They could be removed from the sequence reads by matching the reads to a database containing common lab sources of contamination such as human and pets.

For microbial contaminants not included in the reference database, one could also identify them after the reads are assembled into contigs. If some contigs appear in most of the single cell libraries, and they could not be explained by a dominant species in the community, then they could likely be derived from a common source of contamination.

Some contamination is platform-specific. For example, it is a typical practice to use a multiplex strategy, or sequencing multiple samples (in both a multiwell plate or a droplet format) from the same library, by indexing each sample using a unique, molecular index (UMI), or sequence barcode. A recent paper (Costello *et al.*, 2018) systematically examined the "index switching" problem, that is, a certain percentage (2–10%) of reads from one sample are assigned to the wrong one. This phenomenon is a wide-spread problem, especially for the Illumina sequencing platform. Improving the library construction procedure may reduce the problem. Moreover, combined with a second UMI (dual indexing) should help eliminate this problem because unexpected combinations can be removed.

There are some contamination types that are harder to remove. A low percentage of single cell libraries are not derived from single cells, but instead they are from two, or even a few cells. These doublets, triplets ... are essentially "mini metagenomes", and they should be identified. Tools used for assessing the quality of MAGs that we discussed in the previous chapter can be used here to identify SAGs that contain multiple single-copy marker genes.

9.2.2 *Uneven coverage*

Many existing single-genome *de novo* assembly algorithms have built-in functions to exclude regions in the assembly that have extremely high or low coverage. These regions could be derived from contaminants that have different abundance. High-coverage regions could also be derived from repetitive elements. Low-coverage regions, on the other hand, could be the result of sequencing errors. Excluding these regions where the coverage falls out of the norm reduces the complexity of the de Bruijn graph and makes its traversal manageable. In MDA-amplified single cell genome datasets, sequencing coverage across a genome becomes highly uneven due to a combination of several factors, including random sampling noise and MDA-amplification biases. Chitsaz et al. compared the extent of coverage biases between sequencing datasets derived from either cultured or single-cell sequencing experiments. In their study, the cultured dataset has a roughly normal distribution peaked at 600x coverage with most genomic positions between 450-800x coverage. In contrast, the single cell samples with an average 600x coverage, genomic positions with very small coverage are predominant, and a long thin tail with coverage well above 1000× (Chitsaz *et al.*, 2011). While novel experimental strategies are being developed to reduce this extreme unevenness in genomic coverage, we will discuss a couple of algorithmic innovations to enable single-cell genome assembly. Readers are encouraged to read more about sequencing depth and coverage in genomic analyses in the literature (Sims *et al.*, 2014).

The Velvet-SC algorithm is a modified Velvet genome assembler to salvage low-coverage regions. After the de Bruijn graph is built, instead of removing low-coverage edges using a fixed threshold, it uses an increment threshold that starts at 1 and gradually increases. By merging low-coverage regions with high-coverage regions Velvet-SC avoids eliminating low-coverage regions and is capable of assembling SAGs with over 90% of genes captured (Chitsaz *et al.*, 2011).

Instead of accommodating the uneven coverage of single-cell genome datasets with a specific genome assembler, some algorithms chose to normalize the coverage so that existing genome assemblers can be used. For example, NeatFreq bins reads based on their kmer frequencies. Reads with high kmer frequencies are randomly sampled to reduce the coverage of the genomic regions they originate from (McCorrison *et al.*, 2014). Similar "digital normalization" techniques can also be applied to metagenomic datasets as well, to suppress dominant species and encourage the assembly of rare species (Howe *et al.*, 2014).

9.2.3 *Drop-out genomic regions*

Chitsaz et al. also found that a few percents of the single cell genome had no sequencing coverage at all, despite of an average 600x genome coverage (Chitsaz *et al.*, 2011). The missed representation of some regions is likely caused by amplification biases in amplification or loss of genetic material during the library preparation steps. This problem also exists in single-cell sequencing of human cells, but it is more pronounced in microbial experiments because the genomic DNA only exists in a single copy. Starting with extremely low amounts of genetic material and handling them along the library preparation process is very challenging, sometimes an entire cell can get lost. In theory, there is no way to recover these "drop-out" genomic regions if we have only a single cell for this microbial organism.

If we are lucky, however, a SAG experiment may include several cells from the same organism, giving us an opportunity to recover the full genome of this organism. Mangot et al. sequenced two microbial eukaryotes (14 and 9, respectively) from the Tara Ocean marine community (Mangot *et al.*, 2017). While assembling individual single cells produces incomplete genomes, with genome coverage rates of 18.7% (±9.7) and 14.1% (±5.4) for the two organisms. Increasing sequencing depth did not increase genome recovery. As 18S rDNA sequence similarity is not able to discriminate different strains, the authors used Average Nucleotide Identity (ANI) threshold of 97–99% to group difference cells from the same strain together for coassembly. Adding data from more cells gradually increase genome completeness, and eventually they increased genome completeness to 74.2% and 68.2% for the two organisms (Mangot *et al.*, 2017).

Coassembly of multiple cells may defeat the purpose of single-cell sequencing, as individual genetic variations could get lost. These information could be partially recovered by mapping reads from individual cells back to the assembly. In addition, merging data from multiple cells may inevitably increase the chance of contamination.

9.2.4 *Chimeras*

Chimeras (also called mosaics) are prevalent in genome assemblies from next-generation sequencing datasets. They refer to assembly artifacts with two or more different genomic locations fused at the same location. Chimeras can originate from experimental procedures, for example, two different DNA fragments are ligated at low frequency when sequencing adapters are ligated. They can also be resulted from misassemblies during assembly graph traversal, for example, taking a wrong path in a repetitive region. Many genome assemblers have built-in mechanisms to eliminate chimeras. Rare experimental chimeras can be removed when low-coverage edges are pruned. By searching for abrupt sequencing coverage changes along the assembled genomic sequences, it is possible to identify chimeric contigs and break them at the junctions.

In MDA-amplified single cell genomes, the above chimera elimination strategy would fail. The Phi29 DNA polymerase used in MDA can randomly "jump" to a different DNA template, artificially linking these two templates to create chimeras. These chimeras can get further amplified in subsequent rounds of amplification. Therefore, filtering low-coverage edges may not be as effective as it is in single-genome assembly experiments. To make things worse, as we discussed above, we may want to preserve low-coverage edges in single-cell assembly. Furthermore, the sequencing coverage assumption is also violated in single-cell genome assembly, as discussed above, the uneven coverage is a hallmark in these datasets.

Again, there is not much we could do if there is only a single cell from a particular organism in the microbial community. We could, however, leverage multiple cells from the same organism to eliminate the chimeras discussed above, as chimeras from one cell are unlikely present in other cells due to their random occurrence.

9.3 Leveraging MAGs for SAGs, the Best of two Worlds?

Both assembly methods based on metagenome or single cells successfully produce a large number of genomes, MAGs and SAGs, respectively. They each face their unique challenges. SAG sequencing discussed in this chapter requires expensive lab instrumentation and lengthy experimental procedures. MDA brings the possibility to assemble a single copy of a bacterial genome, but drop-out events and chimeras prevent us from getting a complete and accurate SAG. For metagenome sequencing, limited sequencing depth on complex communities leads to incomplete and contaminated MAGs. How do we choose between these two technologies for metagenomics? This was the exact question Alneberg et al. sought to answer in a recent study (Alneberg *et al.*, 2018).

This study did a comprehensive comparison between the SAG and MAG approaches for recovering prokaryotic genomes. While these two methodologies are in general in strong agreement with each other, MAGs tend to be larger and more complete than their corresponding

SAGs. On the other hand, SAGs can resolve closely related strains, as well as report genetic variants specific to individual cells.

Would it possible to make the two methodologies leverage each other's benefits to overcome each other's disadvantages? Currently, there are no assemblers that take both data types as inputs. There are several "hacks" to combine the two in the literature. For example, one can integrate contigs from a MAG and corresponding SAGs to produce an improved assembly (Mende *et al.*, 2016). One can also recruit corresponding metagenomic sequences to SAGs to improve their completeness (Roux *et al.*, 2014). Or, single-cell data can be used as a guide for metagenome binning process (Arikawa *et al.*, 2021). While gaining some preliminary success, these early efforts increased the assembly complexity by combining two challenging problems into one.

9.4 Future Perspectives

Due to experimental challenges, single-cell RNA-seq of microbial communities is still in its infancy (Imdahl and Saliba, 2020). Obtaining other types of omics from single bacteria is even more challenging. Once these technical hurdles are surpassed, numerous informatics solutions developed for high eukaryote systems will become applicable. New technologies may even enable generating multiple omics data from the same single cell (DNA, RNA, epigenetic modification, etc), providing direct links between a cell's phenotype to its genotype. In addition to these measurements of a single cell, emerging technologies should also make temporal and spatial profiling possible. These technologies will bring new challenges in computational single-cell metagenomics to map the spatial organization of species within a community and track their response to environmental changes.

For complex microbial communities with high species richness and high unevenness, single-cell sequencing may never be able to cover every species due to technical and budget limitations. In the near future, single-cell sequencing will remain an important complementary analysis to metagenome sequencing. More creative ways are needed to combine single-cell sequencing and metagenome sequencing beyond discriminating strains or linking viruses to their hosts. For example, SAGs could form a training for optimizing the metagenome assembly process for the entire community, as they represent a subset of the community. Hypotheses established from metagenomics analysis can be independently validated by targeted single-cell sequencing.

Chapter 10

Interactions Between Microbes and Their Environment

In previous chapters, we have reviewed computational metagenomics methods to explore the taxonomic and functional diversity of a microbial community. These methods provide insight into the genetic "part list" of a community, but they do not reveal how the community functions as a whole, especially in the context of its environment. Within a community, microbial organisms form partners among themselves, and as a team they interact with other teams, their hosts, and their environment. These interactions can be competitive or beneficial in nature, and most of these interactions are likely to be conditional or contextual. For millions of years, they adapt to each other and become part of each other's biological functions. As a community, microbial organisms are subject to selection pressure together. Being able to model both interactions within microbial communities and interactions between a community with its environment is a critical component of bigger questions such as modeling the role of microbes in human health and climate change.

In the final chapter of this book, let us discuss recent advances made in computational metagenomics to understand microbial interactions. I will first review computational methods to study microbial interactions within a community, followed by those to study the interaction between a community with its environment, and finally individual- and community-level metabolic modeling.

10.1 Interactions Within a Community

Studying the interplay between microbes is inherently challenging. Like many genomics problems, studying microbial interactions is also an inherent "curse of dimensionality" problem. People in the clinical genomics field are well aware of this problem, as they routinely rely on a few thousands of individuals to identify genetic variants that are associated with a particular disease out of millions of variants and billions of possible combinations. Here, the curse of dimensionality in microbial interactions is similarly caused by the lack of enough number of samples/observations for the large number of species within a community. Exhaustively quantifying all possible interactions among all species is a combinatorial problem. For a microbiome with n species, there could be $n(n-1)/2$ pairwise interactions. If we consider all possible interactions between n species, then the total number of possible interactions is $2^n - 1$. For a small community with only 100 species, we would have nearly 5,000 possible pairwise interactions, and over 10^{30} possible interactions to consider! This effect is also known as the combinatorial explosion, as n approaches thousands of species, even just considering the pairwise interactions quickly becomes intractable.

It is generally assumed that species interactions within a community are sparse, i.e., most of the species do not interact with each other, and a species only interacts with a very small number of other species. In addition, most of the interactions may not be relevant to the underlying scientific question. Identifying relevant interactions between species within a community is therefore an effective way to greatly reduce the dimensionality and generate testable hypotheses with a limited number of samples. By focusing on species interactions that are relevant to the underlying scientific question (hypothesis-driven), we can avoid the "curse of dimensionality" problem that considers all possible interactions.

There are several types of interactions between microbial species. In an ecological context, two species can manifest a variety of relationships. If they rely on the same resource, they are in a competition relationship. This often happens between closely related species as they tend to have similar nutrition requirements. Distantly related species can form a symbiotic relationship, where they benefit each other (mutualism), or only one gets the benefit without harming the other (commenalism), or one gets the benefit by harming the other (parasitism). In an extreme, if one species feeds on another, the behavior is called predation. Inferring these relationships from metagenomic data is one of the key questions of metagenomics. Below, I will use two examples to demonstrate the power of computational metagenomics in studying species interactions.

10.1.1 *Identifying phage-bacteria pairs*

As eukaryotic cells are infected by viruses, bacterial cells are also commonly infected by bacteriophages, also called phages for simplicity. Identifying phage–host relationships is not only important to understand microbial diversity dynamics, but may also lead to potential novel medical and industrial applications. Identifying phage-bacteria pairs traditionally relies on cultivation approaches, and more recently sequenced-based approaches including single-cell sequencing and Hi-C sequencing as we discussed in Chapter 8. These approaches are either labor-intensive or technically challenging, or both. It would be economical to mine metagenomics datasets to discover phage-host pairs because they are readily available. However, is it possible?

The existence of phages depends on their hosts. If we have multiple independent observations (e.g., metagenome time-series samples), we would expect a large probability that they cooccur in the same sample. By mining 313 samples from the Tara Oceans dataset, Lima-Mendez et al. built species-species co-occurrence networks and inferred 1,869 positive associations between viruses and their hosts (Lima-Mendez et al., 2015). This study may have underestimated the true number of interactions, as rare and low abundance species had been excluded from the network construction, and a simple binary network was used (we will learn more about co-occurrence networks later in this section). Because this approach has no assumption, it is expected to generalize to many communities to infer any type of predation or similar relationships requiring tight cooperation. However, most metagenomics datasets have only a small number of samples, which significantly limits the statistical power of these co-occurrence networks.

The observation that phages and their hosts adopt similar sequence composition profiles can also serve as a generic feature to discover phage-host pairs. This similarity likely reflects the various strategies that phages employ to adapt to their hosts. For example, phages need to avoid certain kmers that are recognized by host restriction enzymes, while sharing a similar codon usage as their hosts to ensure their genes to get efficiently translated. Therefore, recognizing phage-host pairs is equivalent to finding the nearest neighbors of kmer profiles (Roux *et al.*, 2015). Searching similar sequence composition is computationally efficient, and it is robust even with incomplete genomes and small percentages of contamination, two common problems in metagenome-assembled genomes (MAGs). However, closely related species can have similar sequence composition, which may lead to false positives.

We can make additional assumptions to increase the specificity of the prediction. Some phages "borrow" genes or other elements from their hosts, and if the borrowed genes provide a selection advantage, these genes will be retained in the offsprings of the phages. Some phages can also "lend" genes that can are beneficial to their hosts and indirectly increase their own chances of survival (Lindell *et al.*, 2005). These genetic exchanges, if happened recently, leave homologous genes between phages and their hosts. These genes, including auxiliary metabolic genes, tRNAs, etc, can be detected by sequence-alignment based methods to detect homology (Edwards *et al.*, 2016). This method also applies to phages that integrate their entire genomes into their hosts' instead of a few of their genes. The integrated phages, called prophages, share significant homology with free phages if the integration event was recent. These assumptions, however, rely on the availability of genomes with high completeness. In addition, these assumptions can not be universally applied to all phage-host pairs.

We can also utilize some features of the bacterial host defense system to identify their pahges. Bacteria uses the CRISPR–Cas system to "label" invading phages with CRISPR spacers and subsequently use them to recognize future invasions. These spaces can be used to predict bacteria-phage pairs in several studies including this most recent one (Dion *et al.*, 2021).

A more comprehensive evaluation of computational strategies to identify phage-host pairs can be found in a review paper (Edwards *et al.*, 2016). It is worth noting that a few machine learning-based methods that aim to integrate several features we discussed above and obtained encouraging results. As more phage-host pairs are being dis-covered, these methods may benefit from the availability of a larger training set and become mainstream in the near future.

10.1.2 *Identifying other types of relationships*

For a simple community such as the Drosophila gut microbiome, it is possible to exhaustively search all pairwise species interactions via experimental approaches (Gould *et al.*, 2018). This is probably the most reliable way to infer species interactions. For the most complex micro-bial ecosystems, one would have to rely exclusively on computational prediction. These prediction methods fall into two general categories: methods that infer species relationships based on whole genome metabolic models, and methods based on the generalized species co-occurrence network. We will discuss modeling-based approach later in this chapter. Here we will discuss the generalization of the binary co-occurrence networks we mentioned above in phage-host prediction, and explore how they have been used to predict microbial interactions.

Many metagenomics data pipelines output an abundance matrix (sometimes also called taxa abundance table) with each row repre-senting a taxa and each column representing the observed abundance of each taxa in a sample. To build a co-occurrence network, we first derive a square similarity matrix by measuring the similarity between all possible pairs of species over multiple samples using some simi-larity measure (for example, Pearson, Spearman, hypergeometric dis-tribution, and the Jaccard index) (Faust and Raes, 2012). We then only use the significant pairwise relationships (above a threshold) to construct a co-occurrence network for visualization, where nodes are species and edges are their similarity, and the edge weight can rep-resent the strength of the relationship (Faust and Raes, 2012). This method is summarized in Figure 10.1. In the above simple phage-host co-occurrence network, the edge weight was set one if the phage and host are both present in a sample, otherwise it was zero (there-fore a binary network). On datasets with many samples, such as those from the Human Microbiome Project (HMP), co-occurrence net-works can be very powerful to detect species interactions. Faust et al. analyzed 726 samples across 18 body sites, 5,026 HMP samples

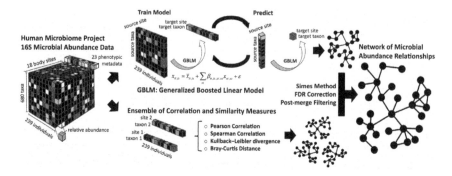

Fig. 10.1 Methodology for constructing co-occurance network. Multidimensional species abundance matrix were analyzed by two complementary approaches: a compendium of Generalized Boosted Linear Model (GBLMs) and an ensemble of similarity and dissimilarity measures. Each approach produced a network in which each node represented a microbial taxon within one body site, and each edge represented a significant association between microbial or whole clade abundances within or across body sites. The two networks were then merged into a single co-occurance network. Please refer the cited publication for details about GBLM fitting and filtering. Reproduced from (Faust and Raes, 2012) with CC-BY 4.0 licence.

to build a global human microbiome network. They applied an ensemble method based on multiple similarity measures to infer 3,005 significant relationships. They were able to capture known relationships as well as predicted many previously uncharacterized interactions (Faust and Raes, 2012).

However, there are a few pitfalls associated with methods based on the co-occurrence network. For example, to measure the significance of the relationship between a species pair in question, a p-value is derived based on a statistical test that tests whether or not the similarity score is drawn from a randomly permuted score distribution. This background distribution, or "null distribution" in the statistics term, may artificially inflate the significance of the p-value if not properly chosen(Connor *et al.*, 2017). As we are doing many such statistical tests for all possible pairs, the p-value threshold for significance is also need to be adjusted for multiple testing to control for false discoveries. The correlation analysis of the abundance data also has some weakness. Because the absolute abundance of species is not known, it is approximated using observed relative fractions of marker genes or species. Friedman and Alm showed that this approximation is unreliable and is prone to false discoveries (Friedman and Alm, 2012). They proposed a Bayesian estimator of the true abundance fractions to correct the observed counts, and then used an iterative approach on the corrected data to derive a better estimation of the true species correlations.

10.2 The Impact of Microbial Communities on Their Environment

The best understood systems to study the interaction between microbial communities and their environment are probably microbiomes associated with animal hosts, especially human. Microbial organisms influence host functions such as pathogen defence, nutrition, metabolism, affect their neurological activities, and even shape their reproduction. The extent of such influence is surprisingly large. According to a study done in mice, a significant portion of the metabolites in host plasma, including those involved in the metabolism of amino acids and organic acids, are directly impacted by its gut microbiome (Wikoff *et al.,* 2009). Understanding the interaction between microbiomes and their hosts plays a central role in understanding how functional diversity is translated into ecological dynamics. These knowledge can also serve as a guide to develop new methods for various applications to intervene disease progression, prevent agricultural degradation, or reduce greenhouse gas emissions.

Adding the complex host biology into the already complex microbiome multiplies their overall complexity and the resulting problem becomes seemly intractable. Taking the human microbiome as an example, it contains trillions of microorganisms colonized in various anatomical regions of the human body. Deciphering the interaction between the human microbiome and its host requires consideration of several dimensions. We need to consider the variations of an individual's genetics ("host-dimension"), as well as the host's lifestyle since the microbiome-host interaction is constantly impacted by changes in the host's lifestyle changes such diet and hygiene, making it necessary to control these environmental factors. We need to consider the different body sites the microbiome resides ("spatial dimension"). Furthermore, we need to consider a "time dimension", as the microbiome also manifests a "development" cycle as their host does: it is established in early childhood, stably maintained in adulthood, and then deteriorates as the host gets old.

Despite the challenges dealing with its complexity or because of, microbiome-host interaction is one of the most active and exciting research areas in computational metagenomics. Although it is currently at a very early stage, I will try to summarize a few strategies here that tackle the complexity. Readers need to be aware that the methods introduced here may be quickly displaced, or totally replaced by better ones as this research field is rapidly evolving.

10.2.1 *Enterotype-based study of microbe-host interactions*

If we assume that the contribution of individual microbes to a phenotype (e.g., diabetes) is additive, we can apply dimensional reduction algorithms such as principal component analysis (PCA) to explore microbial-host interactions. Applying PCA and clustering analysis to 33 human gut microbiome samples formed three distinct clusters (Arumugam *et al.*, 2011). These clusters were designated as "enterotypes", and taxonomic and functional differences among them reflect different combinations of microbes with distinct modes of interaction with the human hosts (Arumugam *et al.*, 2011). If we further assume that the species with greater variation in abundance contributes more to the host phenotype, then the enterotype classification may lead to testable hypotheses of individual species-host interaction. In the above study, each of these three enterotypes are dominated by the abundance variation of three genera: Bacteroides (enterotype 1), Prevotella (enterotype 2), and Ruminococcus (enterotype 3). Enterotype-based analysis is simple to compute, although it ignores the contribution of nonlinear interactions between species to the host phenotype (Costea *et al.*, 2018). Overall, it offers a low-resolution view of microbe-host interactions and paves the way to higher-resolution, function-based views we are going to discuss next.

10.2.2 *Function-based study of microbe-host interactions*

Instead of looking for statistical associations at the species level between microbial species and human phenotype, Tierney et al. decided to "break" the gut microbiome into "microbial features" (species, pathways, and gene families) and use them for association analysis. The total number of features is very large, as they include 6,832 species, 76,251 pathways, and 1,167,504 gene families. They applied a method developed in human genetic analysis, "meta-analyses", that aggregates many datasets from multiple studies to increase statistical power. This type of analysis has been used to search among millions of genetic variants for those associated with certain diseases, a task only possible with a large number of samples. The authors obtained 2,573 human gut microbiome samples from seven disease studies. They found previously unrecognized high-resolution genetic and taxonomic signatures associated with these diseases. Interestingly, they found that gene-level associations are more robust than species-level associations, and gene-level associations are also more reproducible when tested on independent datasets. To combat the multiple hypothesis testing problem (https://en.wikipedia.org/wiki/Multiple_comparisons_problem) and the potential different confounding factors across different datasets, the authors had to use a very conservative threshold to filter for statistically significant features. This may lead to a lower false discovery rate at the expense of a lower recall rate (Tierney *et al.*, 2021).

Function-based approaches offer a high resolution view of the contribution of microbes to their hosts or environments. The large number of genes and gene families drive the "curse of dimensionality" problem worse and computing costs higher.

10.3 The Influence of Environment on Metagenome Communities

In the above discussions, we focused our discussion on the influence of the microbiome on their host's phenotype. Understanding of these influences not only provides insights into the mechanism of interaction, but also inspires new clinical interventions. The converse question is, is microbiome composition determined by host genetics? If so, to what extent host genetics shape microbiome composition? If not, what other environmental factors that drive the dynamic change of the host microbiome? Answers to these questions are important to develop personalized microbiome interventions that are tailored to an individual's genetics.

Again, I will use the human microbiome as an example to discuss strategies addressing the above questions. If the abundance of each microbial organism in the microbiome can be viewed as a microbial quantitative trait locus (mbQTL), the same way many other QTLs such as height or BMI were developed, then quantitative trait mapping methods can be used to look for associated host genetic variations. Several large-scale mbQTL studies in people and mice have started to suggest significant associations between genetic loci and microbiome (reviewed in [Kurilshikov *et al.* (2017)]). However, these studies all faced a major challenge of multiple hypothesis testing. mbQTLs could include hundreds of species, thousands of genetic pathways and gene families if function-based analysis is desired, which significantly increases the likelihood of false discoveries. Most of the findings from these studies could not be replicated (Kurilshikov *et al.*, 2017).

A recent study may challenge the findings related to mbQTL. Rothschild et al. studied microbial–genetic and microbial-environmental associations using 1,046 individuals. Contrary to earlier studies, their results demonstrate that gut microbiome composition is not significantly associated with the host's genetics (Rothschild *et al.*, 2018). Estimated from 2,252 twins, the heritability of the gut microbiome at the taxa level is merely 1.9%. In contrast, they found that there is significant similarity among the microbiomes of genetically unrelated individuals who share a household, and over 20% of the variance in microbiome β-diversity can attribute to environmental factors such as diet and lifestyle. It appears that both microbiome and host genetics independently contribute to the host phenotype, as incorporating microbiome data with human genetic data substantially improves the ability to predict host phenotype (Rothschild *et al.*, 2018).

10.4 Advances in Microbial Community Modeling

Each individual microbial genome is equivalent to an algorithm, as it programs the build of the cellular machinery and all its functions. Given a limited set of inputs (nutrients) in the environment, the genome algorithm maximizes its number of copies through replication (measured by growth or total biomass produced). A microbial community is a pool of such genome algorithms. As we know more about these genome algorithms, we may be able to simulate a digital clone of an organism, or even an entire community in the future. Scientists at Stanford University and the J. Craig Venter Institute actually developed the first digital organism, a simulation of a simple organism called Mycoplasma genitalium in 2012. It models the interactions of 28 categories of molecules — including DNA, RNA, proteins, and metabolites. The comprehensive model predicted many previously unobserved cellular behaviors and molecular processes (Karr *et al.*, 2012).

Currently, we are no way near modeling an unknown bacterium, let alone an entire community with many unknown species. As the British statistician George E. P. Box once said, "All models are wrong, but some are useful". Being able to model a microbial organism or a community, even with many knowledge gaps, may still provide interesting insights into how it functions and its interaction with the environment. In this section, we will briefly overview the research progress in metabolic modeling of microbial organisms and communities.

10.4.1 *Individual microbial genome models*

With the availability of assembled and annotated genomes, it is now possible to generate metabolic networks at a genome scale, even before experimental data is collected. Genome-scale network reconstruction (GENRE) largely consists of two phases. The first phase involves annotating the genome to get a complete list of metabolic reactions. During this phase, annotated genes from the genome of interest are searched against known metabolic databases, such as KEGG (Kyoto Encyclopedia of Genes and Genomes), MetaCyc, and SEED, to identify the enzymes and reactions they catalyse (Feist *et al.*, 2009).

The second phase involves compiling a mathematical representation of these reactions. Starting from a genome-scale metabolic network of every metabolic reaction, we can apply a technique, Flux Balance Analysis (FBA), to explain how the network functions as well as to make predictions about how the network responses to environmental changes. FBA represents the metabolic network as a stoichiometric matrix with rows representing unique metabolites. The metabolic reactions are represented in columns, as a vector of stoichiometric coefficients of the metabolites participating in a reaction. Metabolites consumed (left side of a stoichiometric reaction) take negative coefficients, while the metabolites produced (right side of the reaction) take positive ones and nonparticipating metabolites get zeros (Orth *et al.*, 2010).

The representation of a genome-scale metabolic network as a numerical matrix opens the door to the linear programming world in mathematics where efficient algorithms are available. Matrix computation is also computationally efficient, and the COBRA Toolbox (https://opencobra.github.io/) is a popular toolbox for performing linear calculations. By applying constraints to balance reaction inputs and outputs and keep experimentally observed bounds of the system, it is possible to optimize a phenotype such as biomass production (Orth *et al.*, 2010).

It is worth noting that the reconstruction of a high-quality genome scale metabolic network usually involves many manual steps and literature search, which is very labor and time intensive. It could take several months for several people to construct a network and then many years to iteratively refine the network as new evidence emerges (Thiele and Palsson, 2010). Fortunately, you may find it is not necessary to start building a model from scratch, as over 100 models have been constructed and they are freely available at the BiGG database (http://bigg.ucsd.edu/).

10.4.2 *Microbial community models*

As a genome-scale metabolic model is essential for quantitative prediction of individual organism behavior, a community of these models are central to understand the community function and behavior in changing environments. For most of complex microbial communities such as the human gut microbiome, it is not feasible, given the the time and labor involved, to build a high-quality metabolic network for every member of the community. The above-mentioned model reconstruction process has almost 100 steps, many of those are manual (Thiele and Palsson, 2010). To overcome this limitation, Henry et al. automated most of these steps and developed the Model SEED, a web-based resource available at https://modelseed.org/, to rapidly create new draft metabolic models (Henry *et al.*, 2010). Magnúsdóttir et al. further built a semi-automatic metabolic reconstruction pipeline on top of the draft models from Model SEED and KBase (US Department of Energy Systems Biology Knowledgebase, http://kbase.us). These models were refined using a comparative approach, which propagates any manual refinement to one metabolic reconstruction to other similar processes (Magnúsdóttir et al., 2017). These improvements greatly streamlined and sped up the model construction process. Using this method, the authors were able to generate draft models for 773 human gut bacteria.

With a pool of models in the same microbial community, even in the draft form, now it is possible to predict species interactions. Magnúsdóttir et al. used the models they built and investigated pairwise growth interactions ('co-growth'). They used FBA to compare the growth of every pair in a community to their individual growth and infer their relationships. They were able to discover parasitism, commensalism, or competitive interactions under different environmental conditions such as diet. For example, they found that the high fiber diet led to a higher proportion of commensal and mutualistic interactions (Magnúsdóttir et al., 2017), which provides insights into the role of fiber diet in maintaining a healthy gut microbiome.

Extending the above framework to the entire community is, however, not straightforward. We would need to model the metabolic exchanges between many taxa and run into the above-mentioned "curse of dimensionality" problem. In addition, we would face the challenge of selecting an objective function, as optimizing community growth may contradict optimizing individual growth. A recent study offered one solution to these two challenges. Instead of optimizing the maximal community growth, Diener et al. created a trade-off between optimal community growth and individual growth by limiting community growth to only a fraction of its maximum rate. They then applied a technique called L2 regularization to the individual growth rate (Diener et al., 2020). The resulting human gut microbiome models were able to integrate individual genome-scale metabolic models, dietary information as flux bounds, and taxa abundance estimates from metagenomic data. They applied their models to 186 human microbiomes to analyze the interaction between microbiome and host in healthy people and people with diabetes (Diener et al., 2020).

10.5 Future Perspectives

Advances in assembling the metagenome, annotating gene functions, and reconstructing metabolic networks at the community level start to unravel the natural complexity of microbial ecosystems. Efficient computational approaches have been developed to model many aspects of these systems, including taxonomic and functional diversity, species interactions, and community dynamics in response to environmental changes. However, current efforts have been focused on discovering new species, new functions, and new interactions. As a step towards transtional clinical research, these new discoveries are being associated with various human phenotypes via microbiome-wide association studies to discover new biomarkers for diseases.

So far, the modeling exercises assume a homogeneity among the microbial communities. New evidence increasingly suggests that the local spatial organization of these communities heavily influences intermicrobial, host-microbe, and various community properties. These interactions, in turn, change the spatial organization of the microbial community. With the advent of spatial metagenomics technologies, such as Metagenomic Plot-sampling by sequencing (MaP-seq) (Sheth *et al.*, 2019), the biogeograghy of the intricate networks of microbes and their environment are being mapped. These new evidences, combined with our understanding at the microbial diversity, representing an exciting direction of metagenomics to understand the structural elements that contribute to phenotypic variations of a microbial community (D'Souza, 2020).

As the field of genomics in moving from sequencing or "reading" genomes to synthesizing or "writing" genomes, metagenomics is also likely make the transition from sequencing communities to synthesizing communities. By synthesizing communities, I do not mean mixing several known species and use them as standards for method development. Instead, I refer to a systematic effort to make "designer" communities, first *in silico* and then in real world involving back-and-forth iterative optimizations, with relevant traits useful for clinical intervention of human diseases, optimizing agricultural output, or geochemical applications such as cleaning up pollution. How far are we to an era of synthetic metagenomics? It is probably sooner than what we think.

As we make big strides in synthetic biology, it has been proposed to design synthetic communities, chemically synthesize all members, and then encapsulate them in a yeast cell (Belda *et al.*, 2021). A strong core metagenome can be modelled and synthesized, while habitat-specific metagenomes can be customized by swapping in or out certain metabolic pathways. These models can be further personalized for specific clinical or industrial applications, by including genetic variants that maximize benefits to human hosts or maximize output of an industrial product. Regardless what route will take us there, computational metagenomics would be indispensable for this dream.

Bibliography

Abe, T., Kanaya, S., Kinouchi, M., Ichiba, Y., Kozuki, T., and Ikemura, T. (2003). Informatics for unveiling hidden genome signatures, *Genome research* **13**, 4, pp. 693–702.

Abuín, J. M., Pichel, J. C., Pena, T. F., and Amigo, J. (2015). Bigbwa: approaching the burrows–wheeler aligner to big data technologies, *Bioinformatics* **31**, 24, pp. 4003–4005.

Al-Ajlan, A. and El Allali, A. (2019). Cnn-mgp: Convolutional neural networks for metagenomics gene prediction, *Interdisciplinary Sciences: Computational Life Sciences* **11**, 4, pp. 628–635.

Almeida, A., Nayfach, S., Boland, M., Strozzi, F., Beracochea, M., Shi, Z. J., Pollard, K. S., Sakharova, E., Parks, D. H., Hugenholtz, P., *et al.* (2021). A unified catalog of 204,938 reference genomes from the human gut microbiome, *Nature biotechnology* **39**, 1, pp. 105–114.

Alneberg, J., Karlsson, C. M., Divne, A.-M., Bergin, C., Homa, F., Lindh, M. V., Hugerth, L. W., Ettema, T. J., Bertilsson, S., Andersson, A. F., *et al.* (2018). Genomes from uncultivated prokaryotes: a comparison of metagenome-assembled and single-amplified genomes, *Microbiome* **6**, 1, pp. 1–14.

Antwis, R. E., Griffiths, S. M., Harrison, X. A., Aranega-Bou, P., Arce, A., Bettridge, A. S., Brailsford, F. L., de Menezes, A., Devaynes, A., Forbes, K. M., *et al.* (2017). Fifty important research questions in microbial ecology, *FEMS Microbiology Ecology* **93**, 5, p. fix044.

Aramaki, T., Blanc-Mathieu, R., Endo, H., Ohkubo, K., Kanehisa, M., Goto, S., and Ogata, H. (2020). Kofamkoala: Kegg ortholog assignment based on profile hmm and adaptive score threshold, *Bioinformatics* **36**, 7, pp. 2251–2252.

Arikawa, K., Ide, K., Kogawa, M., Saeki, T., Yoda, T., Endoh, T., Matsuhashi, A., Takeyama, H., and Hosokawa, M. (2021). Recovery of high-quality assembled genomes via single-cell genome-guided binning of metagenome assembly, *bioRxiv* .

Arumugam, M., Raes, J., Pelletier, E., Le Paslier, D., Yamada, T., Mende, D. R., Fernandes, G. R., Tap, J., Bruls, T., Batto, J.-M., *et al.* (2011). Enterotypes of the human gut microbiome, *nature* **473**, 7346, pp. 174–180.

Bankevich, A., Nurk, S., Antipov, D., Gurevich, A. A., Dvorkin, M., Kulikov, A. S., Lesin, V. M., Nikolenko, S. I., Pham, S., Prjibelski, A. D., *et al.* (2012). Spades: a new genome assembly algorithm and its applications to single-cell sequencing, *Journal of computational biology* **19**, 5, pp. 455–477.

Berkeley Lab. (2002). Berkeley UPC: Unified Parallel C, https://upc.lbl.gov/.

Belda, I., Williams, T. C., de Celis, M., Paulsen, I. T., and Pretorius, I. S. (2021). Seeding the idea of encapsulating a representative synthetic metagenome in a single yeast cell, *Nature Communications* **12**, 1, pp. 1–8.

Bernardi, G. and Bernardi, G. (1986). Compositional constraints and genome evolution, *Journal of molecular evolution* **24**, 1-2, pp. 1–11.

Blin, K., Shaw, S., Steinke, K., Villebro, R., Ziemert, N., Lee, S. Y., Medema, M. H., and Weber, T. (2019). antismash 5.0: updates to the secondary metabolite genome mining pipeline, *Nucleic acids research* **47**, W1, pp. W81–W87.

Boisvert, S., Raymond, F., Godzaridis, É., Laviolette, F., and Corbeil, J. (2012). Ray meta: scalable de novo metagenome assembly and profiling, *Genome biology* **13**, 12, p. R122.

Boja, E., Težak, Ž., Zhang, B., Wang, P., Johanson, E., Hinton, D., and Rodriguez, H. (2018). Right data for right patient—a precisionfda nci–cptac multi-omics mislabeling challenge, *Nature medicine* **24**, 9, pp. 1301–1302.

Boon, E., Meehan, C. J., Whidden, C., Wong, D. H.-J., Langille, M. G., and Beiko, R. G. (2014). Interactions in the microbiome: communities of organisms and communities of genes, *FEMS microbiology reviews* **38**, 1, pp. 90–118.

Bowers, R. M., Kyrpides, N. C., Stepanauskas, R., Harmon-Smith, M., Doud, D., Reddy, T., Schulz, F., Jarett, J., Rivers, A. R., Eloe-Fadrosh, E. A., *et al.* (2017). Minimum information about a single amplified genome (misag) and a metagenome-assembled genome (mimag) of bacteria and archaea, *Nature biotechnology* **35**, 8, pp. 725–731.

Buchfink, B., Xie, C., and Huson, D. H. (2015). Fast and sensitive protein alignment using diamond, *Nature methods* **12**, 1, pp. 59–60.

Burrows, M. and Wheeler, D. (1994). A block-sorting lossless data compression algorithm, in *Digital SRC Research Report* (Citeseer).

Calle, M. L. (2019). Statistical analysis of metagenomics data, *Genomics & informatics* **17**, 1.

Carradec, Q., Pelletier, E., Da Silva, C., Alberti, A., Seeleuthner, Y., Blanc-Mathieu, R., Lima-Mendez, G., Rocha, F., Tirichine, L., Labadie, K., *et al.* (2018). A global ocean atlas of eukaryotic genes, *Nature communications* **9**, 1, pp. 1–13.

Chao, A. (1984). Nonparametric estimation of the number of classes in a population, *Scandinavian Journal of statistics*, pp. 265–270.

Chaumeil, P.-A., Mussig, A. J., Hugenholtz, P., and Parks, D. H. (2020). Gtdb-tk: a toolkit to classify genomes with the genome taxonomy database, .

Chitsaz, H., Yee-Greenbaum, J. L., Tesler, G., Lombardo, M.-J., Dupont, C. L., Badger, J. H., Novotny, M., Rusch, D. B., Fraser, L. J., Gormley, N. A., *et al.* (2011). Efficient de novo assembly of single-cell bacterial genomes from short-read data sets, *Nature biotechnology* **29**, 10, pp. 915–921.

Compeau, P. E., Pevzner, P. A., and Tesler, G. (2011). Why are de bruijn graphs useful for genome assembly? *Nature biotechnology* **29**, 11, p. 987.

Connor, N., Barberán, A., and Clauset, A. (2017). Using null models to infer microbial co-occurrence networks, *PloS one* **12**, 5, p. e0176751.

Cormen, T. H., Leiserson, C. E., Rivest, R. L., and Stein, C. (2009). *Introduction to algorithms* (MIT press).

Costea, P. I., Hildebrand, F., Arumugam, M., Bäckhed, F., Blaser, M. J., Bushman, F. D., De Vos, W. M., Ehrlich, S. D., Fraser, C. M., Hattori, M., *et al.* (2018). Enterotypes in the landscape of gut microbial community composition, *Nature microbiology* **3**, 1, pp. 8–16.

Costello, M., Fleharty, M., Abreu, J., Farjoun, Y., Ferriera, S., Holmes, L., Granger, B., Green, L., Howd, T., Mason, T., *et al.* (2018). Characterization and remediation of sample index swaps by non-redundant dual indexing on massively parallel sequencing platforms, *BMC genomics* **19**, 1, pp. 1–10.

Crits-Christoph, A., Diamond, S., Butterfield, C. N., Thomas, B. C., and Banfield, J. F. (2018). Novel soil bacteria possess diverse genes for secondary metabolite biosynthesis, *Nature* **558**, 7710, pp. 440–444.

de Goffau, M. C., Charnock-Jones, D. S., Smith, G. C., and Parkhill, J. (2021). Batch effects account for the main findings of an in utero human intestinal bacterial colonization study, *Microbiome* **9**, 1, pp. 1–7.

Dean, F. B., Hosono, S., Fang, L., Wu, X., Faruqi, A. F., Bray-Ward, P., Sun, Z., Zong, Q., Du, Y., Du, J., *et al.* (2002). Comprehensive human genome amplification using multiple displacement amplification, *Proceedings of the National Academy of Sciences* **99**, 8, pp. 5261–5266.

Dick, G. J., Andersson, A. F., Baker, B. J., Simmons, S. L., Thomas, B. C., Yelton, A. P., and Banfield, J. F. (2009). Community-wide analysis of microbial genome sequence signatures, *Genome biology* **10**, 8, pp. 1–16.

Diener, C., Gibbons, S. M., and Resendis-Antonio, O. (2020). Micom: metagenome-scale modeling to infer metabolic interactions in the gut microbiota, *MSystems* **5**, 1.

Dion, M. B., Plante, P.-L., Zufferey, E., Shah, S. A., Corbeil, J., and Moineau, S. (2021). Streamlining crispr spacer-based bacterial host predictions to decipher the viral dark matter, *Nucleic acids research* **49**, 6, pp. 3127–3138.

D'Souza, G. G. (2020). Phenotypic variation in spatially structured microbial communities: ecological origins and consequences, *Current opinion in biotechnology* **62**, pp. 220–227.

Eddy, S. R. (2011). Accelerated profile hmm searches, *PLoS Comput Biol* **7**, 10, p. e1002195.

Edgar, R. C. (2010). Search and clustering orders of magnitude faster than blast, *Bioinformatics* **26**, 19, pp. 2460–2461.

Edwards, R. A., McNair, K., Faust, K., Raes, J., and Dutilh, B. E. (2016). Computational approaches to predict bacteriophage–host relationships, *FEMS microbiology reviews* **40**, 2, pp. 258–272.

Ehrlich, S. D., Consortium, M., et al. (2011). Metahit: The european union project on metagenomics of the human intestinal tract, in *Metagenomics of the human body* (Springer), pp. 307–316.

Faith, D. P. (1992). Conservation evaluation and phylogenetic diversity, *Biological conservation* **61**, 1, pp. 1–10.

Faust, K. and Raes, J. (2012). Microbial interactions: from networks to models, *Nature Reviews Microbiology* **10**, 8, pp. 538–550.

Feist, A. M., Herrgård, M. J., Thiele, I., Reed, J. L., and Palsson, B. Ø. (2009). Reconstruction of biochemical networks in microorganisms, *Nature Reviews Microbiology* **7**, 2, pp. 129–143.

Ferragina, P. and Manzini, G. (2000). Opportunistic data structures with applications, in *Proceedings 41st Annual Symposium on Foundations of Computer Science* (IEEE), pp. 390–398.

Finotello, F., Mastrorilli, E., and Di Camillo, B. (2018). Measuring the diversity of the human microbiota with targeted next-generation sequencing, *Briefings in bioinformatics* **19**, 4, pp. 679–692.

Franzosa, E. A., Huang, K., Meadow, J. F., Gevers, D., Lemon, K. P., Bohannan, B. J., and Huttenhower, C. (2015). Identifying personal microbiomes using metagenomic codes, *Proceedings of the National Academy of Sciences* **112**, 22, pp. E2930–E2938.

Franzosa, E. A., McIver, L. J., Rahnavard, G., Thompson, L. R., Schirmer, M., Weingart, G., Lipson, K. S., Knight, R., Caporaso, J. G., Segata, N., et al. (2018). Species-level functional profiling of metagenomes and metatranscriptomes, *Nature methods* **15**, 11, pp. 962–968.

Friedman, J. and Alm, E. J. (2012). Inferring correlation networks from genomic survey data, *PLoS Comput Biol* **8**, 9, p. e1002687.

Georganas, E., Egan, R., Hofmeyr, S., Goltsman, E., Arndt, B., Tritt, A., Buluç, A., Oliker, L., and Yelick, K. (2018). Extreme scale de novo metagenome assembly, in *SC18: International Conference for High Performance Computing, Networking, Storage and Analysis* (IEEE), pp. 122–134.

Ghatak, S., King, Z. A., Sastry, A., and Palsson, B. O. (2019). The y-ome defines the 35% of escherichia coli genes that lack experimental evidence of function, *Nucleic acids research* **47**, 5, pp. 2446–2454.

Goldstein, M. and Uchida, S. (2016). A comparative evaluation of unsupervised anomaly detection algorithms for multivariate data, *PloS one* **11**, 4, p. e0152173.

Gould, A. L., Zhang, V., Lamberti, L., Jones, E. W., Obadia, B., Korasidis, N., Gavryushkin, A., Carlson, J. M., Beerenwinkel, N., and Ludington, W. B. (2018). Microbiome interactions shape host fitness, *Proceedings of the National Academy of Sciences* **115**, 51, pp. E11951–E11960.

Groussin, M., Poyet, M., Sistiaga, A., Kearney, S. M., Moniz, K., Noel, M., Hooker, J., Gibbons, S. M., Segurel, L., Froment, A., *et al.* (2021). Elevated rates of horizontal gene transfer in the industrialized human microbiome, *Cell* .

Guo, R., Zhao, Y., Zou, Q., Fang, X., and Peng, S. (2018). Bioinformatics applications on apache spark, *GigaScience* **7**, 8, p. giy098.

Haghi, A., Alvarez, L., Polo, J., Diamantopoulos, D., Hagleitner, C., and Moreto, M. (2020). A hardware/software co-design of k-mer counting using a capi-enabled fpga, in *2020 30th International Conference on Field-Programmable Logic and Applications (FPL)* (IEEE), pp. 57–64.

Harris, J. K., Kelley, S. T., Spiegelman, G. B., and Pace, N. R. (2003). The genetic core of the universal ancestor, *Genome research* **13**, 3, pp. 407–412.

Henry, C. S., Bernstein, H. C., Weisenhorn, P., Taylor, R. C., Lee, J.-Y., Zucker, J., and Song, H.-S. (2016). Microbial community metabolic modeling: a community data-driven network reconstruction, *Journal of cellular physiology* **231**, 11, pp. 2339–2345.

Henry, C. S., DeJongh, M., Best, A. A., Frybarger, P. M., Linsay, B., and Stevens, R. L. (2010). High-throughput generation, optimization and analysis of genome-scale metabolic models, *Nature biotechnology* **28**, 9, pp. 977–982.

Hess, M., Sczyrba, A., Egan, R., Kim, T.-W., Chokhawala, H., Schroth, G., Luo, S., Clark, D. S., Chen, F., Zhang, T., *et al.* (2011). Metagenomic discovery of biomass-degrading genes and genomes from cow rumen, *Science* **331**, 6016, pp. 463–467.

Hie, B., Zhong, E. D., Berger, B., and Bryson, B. (2021). Learning the language of viral evolution and escape, *Science* **371**, 6526, pp. 284–288.

Hofmeyr, S., Egan, R., Georganas, E., Copeland, A. C., Riley, R., Clum, A., Eloe-Fadrosh, E., Roux, S., Goltsman, E., Buluç, A., *et al.* (2020). Terabase-scale metagenome coassembly with metahipmer, *Scientific reports* **10**, 1, pp. 1–11.

Howe, A. C., Jansson, J. K., Malfatti, S. A., Tringe, S. G., Tiedje, J. M., and Brown, C. T. (2014). Tackling soil diversity with the assembly of large, complex metagenomes, *Proceedings of the National Academy of Sciences* **111**, 13, pp. 4904–4909.

Huerta-Cepas, J., Forslund, K., Coelho, L. P., Szklarczyk, D., Jensen, L. J., Von Mering, C., and Bork, P. (2017). Fast genome-wide functional annotation through orthology assignment by eggnog-mapper, *Molecular biology and evolution* **34**, 8, pp. 2115–2122.

Hugenholtz, P., Skarshewski, A., and Parks, D. H. (2016). Genome-based microbial taxonomy coming of age, *Cold Spring Harbor perspectives in biology*
8, 6, p. a018085.

Hughes, J. B., Hellmann, J. J., Ricketts, T. H., and Bohannan, B. J. (2001). Counting the uncountable: statistical approaches to estimating microbial diversity, *Applied and environmental microbiology* **67**, 10, pp. 4399–4406.

Hung, C.-L., Lin, Y.-L., Hua, G.-J., and Hu, Y.-C. (2011). Cloudtss: a tagsnp selection approach on cloud computing, in *International Conference on Grid
and Distributed Computing* (Springer), pp. 525–534.

Huttenhower, C., Gevers, D., Knight, R., Abubucker, S., Badger, J. H., Chinwalla,
A. T., Creasy, H. H., Earl, A. M., FitzGerald, M. G., Fulton, R. S., *et al.*
(2012). Structure, function and diversity of the healthy human microbiome, *nature* **486**, 7402, p. 207.

Hyatt, D., Chen, G.-L., LoCascio, P. F., Land, M. L., Larimer, F. W., and Hauser,
L. J. (2010). Prodigal: prokaryotic gene recognition and translation initi-
ation site identification, *BMC bioinformatics* **11**, 1, pp. 1–11.

Imdahl, F. and Saliba, A.-E. (2020). Advances and challenges in single-cell rna-
seq of microbial communities, *Current Opinion in Microbiology* **57**, pp.
102–110.

Jain, C., Rodriguez-R, L. M., Phillippy, A. M., Konstantinidis, K. T., and Aluru, S.
(2018). High throughput ani analysis of 90k prokaryotic genomes reveals
clear species boundaries, *Nature communications* **9**, 1, pp. 1–8.

Jeong, J., Yun, K., Mun, S., Chung, W.-H., Choi, S.-Y., Lim, M. Y., Hong, C. P., Park,
C., Ahn, Y., Han, K., *et al.* (2021). The effect of taxonomic classification
by full-length 16s rrna sequencing with a synthetic long-read technology,
Scientific reports **11**, 1, pp. 1–12.

Jiang, R., Li, W. V., and Li, J. J. (2020). mbimpute: an accurate and robust imputation method for microbiome data, *bioRxiv* .

Johnson, J. S., Spakowicz, D. J., Hong, B.-Y., Petersen, L. M., Demkowicz, P.,
Chen, L., Leopold, S. R., Hanson, B. M., Agresta, H. O., Gerstein, M., *et al.*
(2019). Evaluation of 16s rrna gene sequencing for species and strain-
level microbiome analysis, *Nature communications* **10**, 1, pp. 1–11.

Jouppi, N. P., Young, C., Patil, N., Patterson, D., Agrawal, G., Bajwa, R.,
Bates, S., Bhatia, S., Boden, N., Borchers, A., *et al.* (2017). In-datacenter
performance analysis of a tensor processing unit, in *2017 ACM/IEEE
44th Annual International Symposium on Computer Architecture (ISCA)*
(IEEE), pp. 1–12.

Kang, D. D., Li, F., Kirton, E., Thomas, A., Egan, R., An, H., and Wang, Z.
(2019). Metabat 2: an adaptive binning algorithm for robust and efficient
genome reconstruction from metagenome assemblies, *PeerJ* **7**, p. e7359.

Karlin, S. and Mrázek, J. (1997). Compositional differences within and between
eukaryotic genomes, *Proceedings of the National Academy of Sciences*
94, 19, pp. 10227–10232.

Karr, J. R., Sanghvi, J. C., Macklin, D. N., Gutschow, M. V., Jacobs, J. M., Bolival Jr, B., Assad-Garcia, N., Glass, J. I., and Covert, M. W. (2012). A whole-cell computational model predicts phenotype from genotype, *Cell* **150**, 2, pp. 389–401.

Kautsar, S. A., Blin, K., Shaw, S., Navarro-Muñoz, J. C., Terlouw, B. R., van der Hooft, J. J., Van Santen, J. A., Tracanna, V., Suarez Duran, H. G., Pascal Andreu, V., *et al.* (2020). Mibig 2.0: a repository for biosynthetic gene clusters of known function, *Nucleic acids research* **48**, D1, pp. D454–D458.

Kent, W. J. (2002). Blat—the blast-like alignment tool, *Genome research* **12**, 4, pp. 656–664.

Kho, Z. Y. and Lal, S. K. (2018). The human gut microbiome–a potential controller of wellness and disease, *Frontiers in microbiology* **9**, p. 1835.

Kloosterman, A. M., Cimermancic, P., Elsayed, S. S., Du, C., Hadjithomas, M., Donia, M. S., Fischbach, M. A., van Wezel, G. P., and Medema, M. H. (2020). Expansion of ripp biosynthetic space through integration of pangenomics and machine learning uncovers a novel class of lantibiotics, *PLoS biology* **18**, 12, p. e3001026.

Knight, R., Jansson, J., Field, D., Fierer, N., Desai, N., Fuhrman, J. A., Hugenholtz, P., Van Der Lelie, D., Meyer, F., Stevens, R., *et al.* (2012). Unlocking the potential of metagenomics through replicated experimental design, *Nature biotechnology* **30**, 6, pp. 513–520.

Knights, D., Kuczynski, J., Koren, O., Ley, R. E., Field, D., Knight, R., DeSantis, T. Z., and Kelley, S. T. (2011). Supervised classification of microbiota mitigates mislabeling errors, *The ISME journal* **5**, 4, pp. 570–573.

Kolmogorov, M., Bickhart, D. M., Behsaz, B., Gurevich, A., Rayko, M., Shin, S. B., Kuhn, K., Yuan, J., Polevikov, E., Smith, T. P., *et al.* (2020). metaflye: scalable long-read metagenome assembly using repeat graphs, *Nature Methods* **17**, 11, pp. 1103–1110.

Konstantinidis, K. T. and Tiedje, J. M. (2005). Genomic insights that advance the species definition for prokaryotes, *Proceedings of the National Academy of Sciences* **102**, 7, pp. 2567–2572.

Koren, S., Walenz, B. P., Berlin, K., Miller, J. R., Bergman, N. H., and Phillippy, A. M. (2017). Canu: scalable and accurate long-read assembly via adaptive k-mer weighting and repeat separation, *Genome research* **27**, 5, pp. 722–736.

Krizhevsky, A., Sutskever, I., and Hinton, G. E. (2012). Imagenet classification with deep convolutional neural networks, *Advances in neural information processing systems* **25**, pp. 1097–1105.

Kurilshikov, A., Wijmenga, C., Fu, J., and Zhernakova, A. (2017). Host genetics and gut microbiome: challenges and perspectives, *Trends in immunology* **38**, 9, pp. 633–647.

Lam, K. N., Cheng, J., Engel, K., Neufeld, J. D., and Charles, T. C. (2015). Current and future resources for functional metagenomics, *Frontiers in microbiology* **6**, p. 1196.

Langmead, B. and Salzberg, S. L. (2012). Fast gapped-read alignment with bowtie 2, *Nature methods* **9**, 4, p. 357.

Lee, K. Y., Park, J. M., Kim, T. Y., Yun, H., and Lee, S. Y. (2010). The genome-scale metabolic network analysis of zymomonas mobilis zm4 explains physiological features and suggests ethanol and succinic acid production strategies, *Microbial cell factories* **9**, 1, pp. 1–12.

Levy Karin, E., Mirdita, M., and Söding, J. (2020). Metaeuk—sensitive, high-throughput gene discovery, and annotation for large-scale eukaryotic metagenomics, *Microbiome* **8**, pp. 1–15.

Li, H. (2016). Minimap and miniasm: fast mapping and de novo assembly for noisy long sequences, *Bioinformatics* **32**, 14, pp. 2103–2110.

Li, H. (2018). Minimap2: pairwise alignment for nucleotide sequences, *Bioinformatics* **34**, 18, pp. 3094–3100.

Li, H. and Durbin, R. (2009). Fast and accurate short read alignment with burrows–wheeler transform, *bioinformatics* **25**, 14, pp. 1754–1760.

Li, J., Jia, H., Cai, X., Zhong, H., Feng, Q., Sunagawa, S., Arumugam, M., Kultima, J. R., Prifti, E., Nielsen, T., *et al.* (2014). An integrated catalog of reference genes in the human gut microbiome, *Nature biotechnology* **32**, 8, pp. 834–841.

Lima-Mendez, G., Faust, K., Henry, N., Decelle, J., Colin, S., Carcillo, F., Chaffron, S., Ignacio-Espinosa, J. C., Roux, S., Vincent, F., *et al.* (2015). Determinants of community structure in the global plankton interactome, *Science* **348**, 6237.

Lindell, D., Jaffe, J. D., Johnson, Z. I., Church, G. M., and Chisholm, S. W. (2005). Photosynthesis genes in marine viruses yield proteins during host infection, *Nature* **438**, 7064, pp. 86–89.

Lozupone, C. A., Hamady, M., Kelley, S. T., and Knight, R. (2007). Quantitative and qualitative β diversity measures lead to different insights into factors that structure microbial communities, *Applied and environmental microbiology* **73**, 5, pp. 1576–1585.

Lu, J. and Salzberg, S. L. (2020). Ultrafast and accurate 16s rrna microbial community analysis using kraken 2, *Microbiome* **8**, 1, pp. 1–11.

Magnúsdóttir, S., Heinken, A., Kutt, L., Ravcheev, D. A., Bauer, E., Noronha, A., Greenhalgh, K., Jäger, C., Baginska, J., Wilmes, P., *et al.* (2017). Generation of genome-scale metabolic reconstructions for 773 members of the human gut microbiota, *Nature biotechnology* **35**, 1, pp. 81–89.

Mäkinen, V., Belazzougui, D., Cunial, F., and Tomescu, A. I. (2015). *Genome-scale algorithm design* (Cambridge University Press).

Mangot, J.-F., Logares, R., Sánchez, P., Latorre, F., Seeleuthner, Y., Mondy, S., Sieracki, M. E., Jaillon, O., Wincker, P., De Vargas, C., *et al.* (2017). Accessing the genomic information of unculturable oceanic picoeukaryotes by combining multiple single cells, *Scientific Reports* **7**, 1, pp. 1–12.

Mazumder, R., Hastie, T., and Tibshirani, R. (2010). Spectral regularization algorithms for learning large incomplete matrices, *The Journal of Machine Learning Research* **11**, pp. 2287–2322.

McCorrison, J. M., Venepally, P., Singh, I., Fouts, D. E., Lasken, R. S., and Methé, B. A. (2014). Neatfreq: reference-free data reduction and coverage normalization for de novo sequence assembly, *BMC bioinformatics* **15**, 1, pp. 1–12.

Medema, M. H., Blin, K., Cimermancic, P., de Jager, V., Zakrzewski, P., Fischbach, M. A., Weber, T., Takano, E., and Breitling, R. (2011). antismash: rapid identification, annotation and analysis of secondary metabolite biosynthesis gene clusters in bacterial and fungal genome sequences, *Nucleic acids research* **39**, suppl_2, pp. W339–W346.

Mende, D. R., Aylward, F. O., Eppley, J. M., Nielsen, T. N., and DeLong, E. F. (2016). Improved environmental genomes via integration of metagenomic and single-cell assemblies, *Frontiers in microbiology* **7**, p. 143.

Mikheenko, A., Saveliev, V., and Gurevich, A. (2016). Metaquast: evaluation of metagenome assemblies, *Bioinformatics* **32**, 7, pp. 1088–1090.

Mitchell, K., Brito, J. J., Mandric, I., Wu, Q., Knyazev, S., Chang, S., Martin, L. S., Karlsberg, A., Gerasimov, E., Littman, R., *et al.* (2020). Benchmarking of computational error-correction methods for next-generation sequencing data, *Genome biology* **21**, 1, pp. 1–13.

Myers, E. W. (1995). Toward simplifying and accurately formulating fragment assembly, *Journal of Computational Biology* **2**, 2, pp. 275–290.

Nagarajan, N. and Pop, M. (2009). Parametric complexity of sequence assembly: theory and applications to next generation sequencing, *Journal of computational biology* **16**, 7, pp. 897–908.

Newman, D. J. and Cragg, G. M. (2012). Natural products as sources of new drugs over the 30 years from 1981 to 2010, *Journal of natural products* **75**, 3, pp. 311–335.

Nicholas, A. B., Avila-Herrera, A., Allen, J. E., Singh, N., Sielaff, A. C., Jaing, C., and Venkateswaran, K. (2017). Whole metagenome profiles of particulates collected from the international space station, *Microbiome* **5**, 1, pp. 1–19.

Nordberg, H., Bhatia, K., Wang, K., and Wang, Z. (2013). Biopig: a hadoop-based analytic toolkit for large-scale sequence data, *Bioinformatics* **29**, 23, pp. 3014–3019.

Northcutt, C. G., Athalye, A., and Mueller, J. (2021). Pervasive label errors in test sets destabilize machine learning benchmarks, *arXiv preprint arXiv:2103.14749* .

Ondov, B. D., Treangen, T. J., Melsted, P., Mallonee, A. B., Bergman, N. H., Koren, S., and Phillippy, A. M. (2016). Mash: fast genome and metagenome distance estimation using minhash, *Genome biology* **17**, 1, pp. 1–14.

Orth, J. D., Thiele, I., and Palsson, B. Ø. (2010). What is flux balance analysis? *Nature biotechnology* **28**, 3, pp. 245–248.

Parks, D. H., Imelfort, M., Skennerton, C. T., Hugenholtz, P., and Tyson, G. W. (2015). Checkm: assessing the quality of microbial genomes recovered from isolates, single cells, and metagenomes, *Genome research* **25**, 7, pp. 1043–1055.

Pasolli, E., Asnicar, F., Manara, S., Zolfo, M., Karcher, N., Armanini, F., Beghini, F., Manghi, P., Tett, A., Ghensi, P., *et al.* (2019). Extensive unexplored human microbiome diversity revealed by over 150,000 genomes from metagenomes spanning age, geography, and lifestyle, *Cell* **176**, 3, pp. 649–662.

Peters, D., Luo, X., Qiu, K., and Liang, P. (2012). Speeding up large-scale next generation sequencing data analysis with pbwa, *J Appl Bioinform Comput Biol* **1**, 1, pp. 10–4172.

Ramírez-Flandes, S., González, B., and Ulloa, O. (2019). Redox traits characterize the organization of global microbial communities, *Proceedings of the National Academy of Sciences* **116**, 9, pp. 3630–3635.

Randall, D. W., Kieswich, J., Swann, J., McCafferty, K., Thiemermann, C., Curtis, M., Hoyles, L., and Yaqoob, M. M. (2019). Batch effect exerts a bigger influence on the rat urinary metabolome and gut microbiota than uraemia: a cautionary tale, *Microbiome* **7**, 1, pp. 1–10.

Reimand, J., Isserlin, R., Voisin, V., Kucera, M., Tannus-Lopes, C., Rostamianfar, A., Wadi, L., Meyer, M., Wong, J., Xu, C., *et al.* (2019). Pathway enrichment analysis and visualization of omics data using g: Profiler, gsea, cytoscape and enrichmentmap, *Nature protocols* **14**, 2, pp. 482–517.

Rinke, C., Schwientek, P., Sczyrba, A., Ivanova, N. N., Anderson, I. J., Cheng, J.-F., Darling, A., Malfatti, S., Swan, B. K., Gies, E. A., *et al.* (2013). Insights into the phylogeny and coding potential of microbial dark matter, *Nature* **499**, 7459, pp. 431–437.

Roberts, M., Hayes, W., Hunt, B. R., Mount, S. M., and Yorke, J. A. (2004). Reducing storage requirements for biological sequence comparison, *Bioinformatics* **20**, 18, pp. 3363–3369.

Robinson, S. L., Piel, J., and Sunagawa, S. (2021). A roadmap for metagenomic enzyme discovery, *Natural Product Reports* .

Rodriguez-R, L. M., Castro, J. C., Kyrpides, N. C., Cole, J. R., Tiedje, J. M., and Konstantinidis, K. T. (2018). How much do rrna gene surveys underestimate extant bacterial diversity? *Applied and environmental microbiology* **84**, 6.

Rothschild, D., Weissbrod, O., Barkan, E., Kurilshikov, A., Korem, T., Zeevi, D., Costea, P. I., Godneva, A., Kalka, I. N., Bar, N., *et al.* (2018). Environment dominates over host genetics in shaping human gut microbiota, *Nature* **555**, 7695, pp. 210–215.

Roux, S., Hallam, S. J., Woyke, T., and Sullivan, M. B. (2015). Viral dark matter and virus–host interactions resolved from publicly available microbial genomes, *elife* **4**, p. e08490.

Roux, S., Hawley, A. K., Beltran, M. T., Scofield, M., Schwientek, P., Stepanauskas, R., Woyke, T., Hallam, S. J., and Sullivan, M. B. (2014). Ecology and evolution of viruses infecting uncultivated sup05 bacteria as revealed by single-cell-and meta-genomics, *elife* **3**, p. e03125.

Salzberg, S. L. (2019). Next-generation genome annotation: we still struggle to get it right, .

Sanders, H. L. (1968). Marine benthic diversity: a comparative study, *The American Naturalist* **102**, 925, pp. 243–282.

Segata, N., Waldron, L., Ballarini, A., Narasimhan, V., Jousson, O., and Huttenhower, C. (2012). Metagenomic microbial community profiling using unique clade-specific marker genes, *Nature methods* **9**, 8, pp. 811–814.

Sender, R., Fuchs, S., and Milo, R. (2016). Revised estimates for the number of human and bacteria cells in the body, *PLoS biology* **14**, 8, p. e1002533.

Sheth, R. U., Li, M., Jiang, W., Sims, P. A., Leong, K. W., and Wang, H. H. (2019). Spatial metagenomic characterization of microbial biogeography in the gut, *Nature biotechnology* **37**, 8, pp. 877–883.

Shi, L., Meng, X., Tseng, E., Mascagni, M., and Wang, Z. (2018). Sparc: scalable sequence clustering using apache spark, *Bioinformatics* **35**, 5, pp. 760–768.

Shi, L., Wang, Z., Yu, W., and Meng, X. (2017). A case study of tuning mapreduce for efficient bioinformatics in the cloud, *Parallel Computing* **61**, pp. 83–95.

Shi, W., Moon, C. D., Leahy, S. C., Kang, D., Froula, J., Kittelmann, S., Fan, C., Deutsch, S., Gagic, D., Seedorf, H., *et al.* (2014). Methane yield phenotypes linked to differential gene expression in the sheep rumen microbiome, *Genome research* **24**, 9, pp. 1517–1525.

Sieber, C. M., Probst, A. J., Sharrar, A., Thomas, B. C., Hess, M., Tringe, S. G., and Banfield, J. F. (2018). Recovery of genomes from metagenomes via a dereplication, aggregation and scoring strategy, *Nature microbiology* **3**, 7, pp. 836–843.

Simon, H. Y., Siddle, K. J., Park, D. J., and Sabeti, P. C. (2019). Benchmarking metagenomics tools for taxonomic classification, *Cell* **178**, 4, pp. 779–794.

Sims, D., Sudbery, I., Ilott, N. E., Heger, A., and Ponting, C. P. (2014). Sequencing depth and coverage: key considerations in genomic analyses, *Nature Reviews Genetics* **15**, 2, pp. 121–132.

Singer, E., Wagner, M., and Woyke, T. (2017). Capturing the genetic makeup of the active microbiome in situ, *The ISME journal* **11**, 9, pp. 1949–1963.

Singleton, C. M., Petriglieri, F., Kristensen, J. M., Kirkegaard, R. H., Michaelsen, T. Y., Andersen, M. H., Kondrotaite, Z., Karst, S. M., Dueholm, M. S., Nielsen, P. H., *et al.* (2020). Connecting structure to function with the recovery of over 1000 high-quality activated sludge metagenome-assembled genomes encoding full-length rrna genes using long-read sequencing, *bioRxiv* .

Song, L., Florea, L., and Langmead, B. (2014). Lighter: fast and memory-efficient sequencing error correction without counting, *Genome biology* **15**, 11, pp. 1–13.

Spanogiannopoulos, P., Bess, E. N., Carmody, R. N., and Turnbaugh, P. J. (2016). The microbial pharmacists within us: a metagenomic view of xenobiotic metabolism, *Nature Reviews Microbiology* **14**, 5, p. 273.

Staley, J. T. and Konopka, A. (1985). Measurement of in situ activities of non-photosynthetic microorganisms in aquatic and terrestrial habitats, *Annual review of microbiology* **39**, 1, pp. 321–346.

Steinegger, M., Meier, M., Mirdita, M., Vöhringer, H., Haunsberger, S. J., and Söding, J. (2019a). Hh-suite3 for fast remote homology detection and deep protein annotation, *BMC bioinformatics* **20**, 1, pp. 1–15.

Steinegger, M., Mirdita, M., and Söding, J. (2019b). Protein-level assembly increases protein sequence recovery from metagenomic samples many-fold, *Nature methods* **16**, 7, pp. 603–606.

Steinegger, M. and Söding, J. (2018). Clustering huge protein sequence sets in linear time, *Nature communications* **9**, 1, pp. 1–8.

Stephens, Z. D., Lee, S. Y., Faghri, F., Campbell, R. H., Zhai, C., Efron, M. J., Iyer, R., Schatz, M. C., Sinha, S., and Robinson, G. E. (2015). Big data: astronomical or genomical? *PLoS biology* **13**, 7, p. e1002195.

Sunagawa, S., Acinas, S. G., Bork, P., Bowler, C., Eveillard, D., Gorsky, G., Guidi, L., Iudicone, D., Karsenti, E., Lombard, F., *et al.* (2020). Tara oceans: towards global ocean ecosystems biology, *Nature Reviews Microbiology* **18**, 8, pp. 428–445.

Tang, D., Wang, M., Zheng, W., and Wang, H. (2014). Rapidmic: rapid computation of the maximal information coefficient, *Evolutionary bioinformatics* **10**, pp. EBO–S13121.

Tatusov, R. L., Koonin, E. V., and Lipman, D. J. (1997). A genomic perspective on protein families, *Science* **278**, 5338, pp. 631–637.

Telenti, A., Pierce, L. C., Biggs, W. H., Di Iulio, J., Wong, E. H., Fabani, M. M., Kirkness, E. F., Moustafa, A., Shah, N., Xie, C., *et al.* (2016). Deep sequencing of 10,000 human genomes, *Proceedings of the National Academy of Sciences* **113**, 42, pp. 11901–11906.

Thiele, I. and Palsson, B. Ø. (2010). A protocol for generating a high-quality genome-scale metabolic reconstruction, *Nature protocols* **5**, 1, p. 93.

Tibshirani, R., Hastie, T., Narasimhan, B., and Chu, G. (2002). Diagnosis of multiple cancer types by shrunken centroids of gene expression, *Proceedings of the National Academy of Sciences* **99**, 10, pp. 6567–6572.

Tierney, B. T., Tan, Y., Kostic, A. D., and Patel, C. J. (2021). Gene-level metagenomic architectures across diseases yield high-resolution microbiome diagnostic indicators, *Nature communications* **12**, 1, pp. 1–12.

Tierney, B. T., Yang, Z., Luber, J. M., Beaudin, M., Wibowo, M. C., Baek, C., Mehlenbacher, E., Patel, C. J., and Kostic, A. D. (2019). The landscape of genetic content in the gut and oral human microbiome, *Cell host & microbe* **26**, 2, pp. 283–295.

Turnbaugh, P. J., Hamady, M., Yatsunenko, T., Cantarel, B. L., Duncan, A., Ley, R. E., Sogin, M. L., Jones, W. J., Roe, B. A., Affourtit, J. P., *et al.* (2009). A core gut microbiome in obese and lean twins, *nature* **457**, 7228, pp. 480–484.

Tyson, G. W., Chapman, J., Hugenholtz, P., Allen, E. E., Ram, R. J., Richardson, P. M., Solovyev, V. V., Rubin, E. M., Rokhsar, D. S., and Banfield, J. F. (2004). Community structure and metabolism through reconstruction of microbial genomes from the environment, *Nature* **428**, 6978, pp. 37–43.

Venter, J. C., Remington, K., Heidelberg, J. F., Halpern, A. L., Rusch, D., Eisen, J. A., Wu, D., Paulsen, I., Nelson, K. E., Nelson, W., *et al.* (2004). Environmental genome shotgun sequencing of the sargasso sea, *science* **304**, 5667, pp. 66–74.

Villa, M. M., Bloom, R. J., Silverman, J. D., Durand, H. K., Jiang, S., Wu, A., Huang, S., You, L., and David, L. A. (2019). High-throughput isolation and culture of human gut bacteria with droplet microfluidics, *bioRxiv*, p. 630822.

Wang, D. and Bodovitz, S. (2010). Single cell analysis: the new frontier in 'omics', *Trends in biotechnology* **28**, 6, pp. 281–290.

Wang, Y., Shi, Q., Yang, P., Zhang, C., Mortuza, S., Xue, Z., Ning, K., and Zhang, Y. (2019a). Fueling ab initio folding with marine metagenomics enables structure and function predictions of new protein families, *Genome biology* **20**, 1, pp. 1–14.

Wang, Z., Ho, H., Egan, R., Yao, S., Kang, D., Froula, J., Sevim, V., Schulz, F., Shay, J. E., Macklin, D., *et al.* (2019b). A new method for rapid genome classification, clustering, visualization, and novel taxa discovery from metagenome, *BioRxiv*, p. 812917.

Wenger, A. M., Peluso, P., Rowell, W. J., Chang, P.-C., Hall, R. J., Concepcion, G. T., Ebler, J., Fungtammasan, A., Kolesnikov, A., Olson, N. D., *et al.* (2019). Accurate circular consensus long-read sequencing improves variant detection and assembly of a human genome, *Nature biotechnology* **37**, 10, pp. 1155–1162.

Wick, R. R., Schultz, M. B., Zobel, J., and Holt, K. E. (2015). Bandage: interactive visualization of de novo genome assemblies, *Bioinformatics* **31**, 20, pp. 3350–3352.

Wikipedia (2019a). Field-programmable gate array — Wikipedia, the free encyclopedia, http://en.wikipedia.org/w/index.php?title=Field-programmable%20gate%20array&oldid=916655903, [Online; accessed 30-September-2019].

Wikipedia (2019b). Graphics processing unit — Wikipedia, the free encyclopedia, http://en.wikipedia.org/w/index.php?title=Graphics%20processing%20unit&oldid=916685262, [Online; accessed 30-September-2019].

Wikipedia (2019c). Message Passing Interface — Wikipedia, the free encyclopedia, http://en.wikipedia.org/w/index.php?title=Message%20Passing%20Interface&oldid=914967971, [Online; accessed 29-September-2019].

Wikipedia (2019d). Partitioned global address space — Wikipedia, the free encyclopedia, http://en.wikipedia.org/w/index.php?title=Partitioned%20global%20address%20space&oldid=865134447, [Online; accessed 29-September-2019].

Wikoff, W. R., Anfora, A. T., Liu, J., Schultz, P. G., Lesley, S. A., Peters, E. C., and Siuzdak, G. (2009). Metabolomics analysis reveals large effects of gut microflora on mammalian blood metabolites, *Proceedings of the national academy of sciences* **106**, 10, pp. 3698–3703.

Woloszynek, S., Zhao, Z., Chen, J., and Rosen, G. L. (2019). 16s rrna sequence embeddings: Meaningful numeric feature representations of nucleotide sequences that are convenient for downstream analyses, *PLoS computational biology* **15**, 2, p. e1006721.

Wood, D. E. and Salzberg, S. L. (2014). Kraken: ultrafast metagenomic sequence classification using exact alignments, *Genome biology* **15**, 3, pp. 1–12.

Xu, Y. and Zhao, F. (2018). Single-cell metagenomics: challenges and applications, *Protein & cell* **9**, 5, pp. 501–510.

Ye, Y. and Doak, T. G. (2009). A parsimony approach to biological pathway reconstruction/inference for genomes and metagenomes, *PLoS computational biology* **5**, 8, p. e1000465.

Yeoh, Y. K., Zuo, T., Lui, G. C.-Y., Zhang, F., Liu, Q., Li, A. Y., Chung, A. C., Cheung, C. P., Tso, E. Y., Fung, K. S., *et al.* (2021). Gut microbiota composition reflects disease severity and dysfunctional immune responses in patients with covid-19, *Gut* .

Zhang, H., Jain, C., and Aluru, S. (2020). A comprehensive evaluation of long read error correction methods, *BMC genomics* **21**, 6, pp. 1–15.

Zhang, K., Martiny, A. C., Reppas, N. B., Barry, K. W., Malek, J., Chisholm, S. W., and Church, G. M. (2006). Sequencing genomes from single cells by polymerase cloning, *Nature biotechnology* **24**, 6, pp. 680–686.

Zhang, K.-Y., Gao, Y.-Z., Du, M.-Z., Liu, S., Dong, C., and Guo, F.-B. (2019). Vgas: a viral genome annotation system, *Frontiers in microbiology* **10**, p. 184.

Zhao, L., Xie, J., Bai, L., Chen, W., Wang, M., Zhang, Z., Wang, Y., Zhao, Z., and Li, J. (2018). Mining statistically-solid k-mers for accurate ngs error correction, *BMC genomics* **19**, 10, pp. 1–10.

Zhao, Y., Tang, H., and Ye, Y. (2012). Rapsearch2: a fast and memory-efficient protein similarity search tool for next-generation sequencing data, *Bioinformatics* **28**, 1, pp. 125–126.

Zheng, Y., Kamil, A., Driscoll, M. B., Shan, H., and Yelick, K. (2014). Upc++: a pgas extension for c++, in *2014 IEEE 28th International Parallel and Distributed Processing Symposium* (IEEE), pp. 1105–1114.

Zhou, W., Li, R., Yuan, S., Liu, C., Yao, S., Luo, J., and Niu, B. (2017). Metaspark: a spark-based distributed processing tool to recruit metagenomic reads to reference genomes, *Bioinformatics* **33**, 7, pp. 1090–1092.

Zhu, W., Lomsadze, A., and Borodovsky, M. (2010). Ab initio gene identification in metagenomic sequences, *Nucleic acids research* **38**, 12, pp. e132–e132.

Zou, Q., Hu, Q., Guo, M., and Wang, G. (2015). Halign: Fast multiple similar dna/rna sequence alignment based on the centre star strategy, *Bioinformatics* **31**, 15, pp. 2475–2481.

Index

CPSIA information can be obtained
at www.ICGtesting.com
Printed in the USA
BVHW091154260422
635046BV00002B/54

9 789811 242465